FUNNY FOLK

'In County Durham, where I grew up, we have a saying: "There's nowt so funny as folk". I remember hearing my father end his numerous stories with it, and I suppose his gusty pleasure in recounting the comic behaviour of ordinary people has infected me. At any rate, I have always enjoyed what folklore experts call jocular tales.

This collection of some of my favourites includes familiar stories that have been told for hundreds of years as well as anecdotes from our own times. Folk tales are not museum pieces preserved from days gone by. They tell about people living now as much as about people long dead, and they often begin as street-corner jokes that grow as teller after teller adds his own colour and detail. That's why I've put in some squibs and even items from newspapers. They are folk tales at their beginnings.'

AIDAN CHAMBERS

Aidan Chambers

FUNNY FOLK

A Book of Comic Tales

Illustrated by
Trevor Stubley

FONTANA · LIONS

First published 1976 by
William Heinemann Ltd
First published in Lions 1978
by William Collins Sons & Co Ltd
14 St James's Place, London SW1
Second impression July 1979

Printed in Great Britain by
Richard Clay (The Chaucer Press) Ltd
Bungay, Suffolk

For my mother and father :
two funny folk

CONTENTS

Three Noodles

There was once an old woman who went off to visit a neighbour, leaving her daughter to get the dinner ready. When the old woman got back, she found nothing in order. The dinner wasn't made and her daughter was sitting by the fire, crying.

'Heyday! What now?' asked the old woman.

'Why, do you know,' said the girl, 'as I was going to cook the dinner a brick fell down the chimney, and, you know, it *might* have killed me!'

'Good gracious!' said the old woman. 'Think of that!' And she sat down beside her daughter and burst out crying as well.

In a while the husband came home from work and found his wife and daughter weeping and his dinner not made.

'What's the matter here?' he asked. 'Why all these tears?'

'Do you know what happened to our Sally?' said the old woman. 'She was just going to make the dinner when a brick fell down the chimney, and, you know, it *might* have killed her!'

'Never!' said the husband. 'What a terrible carry-on!'

Just then Sally's sweetheart came in. Seeing the to-do, he called out, 'Now then, what's on here? Why the commotion?'

'Do you know what?' said the father. 'As our Sally was getting the dinner, a brick fell down the chimney, and, you know, it *might* have killed her!'

'Well of all the fools I've seen,' said the young man, 'you three are the daftest. And when I find three dafter than you, I'll come back and marry your daughter.'

So away he went.

Soon he came to a cottage. The door was open and he could see into the kitchen. Inside was an old woman, wailing and moaning and tugging on a rope. One end of the rope was tied round the oven, and the old woman was heaving on the other end, trying to drag the oven across the floor to the table where some cakes were waiting to be baked.

'Oh, you ninny!' the young man called out. 'You should take the cakes to the oven, not pull the oven to the cakes.'

The old woman stopped her bawling and her heaving and stared at the young man. 'Well I never,' she said after a minute. 'I didn't think of that.'

'That's fool number one,' thought the young man to himself and set off again on his search.

This time he went a long way before he came to an old woman with her shoulder pressed hard against the back end of a skinny cow. She was huffing and puffing as she shoved; the cow was bellowing and digging its hooves into the ground.

'What's on?' asked the young man.

'I'm trying to get 'er up yon,' said the old woman between puffs and huffs and shoves, and she pointed to the roof of her cottage.

'What do you want her up there for?' asked the young man.

'Why, because there's fresh grass growing on my thatch,' said the old woman. 'And 'appen eating it will put some flesh on this mangy beast.'

The young man looked up at the roof, and sure enough thick clumps of succulent grass were growing there.

'But you noodle,' he said, 'why don't you cut the grass and throw it down to the cow instead of trying to get the cow up to the grass?'

The old woman stopped her pushing, looked from the young man to the roof, from the roof to the cow, and from the cow to the young man again.

'There's a bright laddie,' she said, and went off to find a ladder.

'Fool number two,' thought the young man to himself, 'but it will be a long time before I meet such another, I'll bet.'

But the world isn't so short of fools, and it wasn't long before he came to where a man was trying to put on his trousers. Instead of holding them in his hands, he had propped them up with sticks and was taking run after run, jumping in the air, and hoping to land with his legs in the trousers. But he never did.

'Well, here's a right fool indeed,' said the young man. 'A bigger fool than all the others put together.'

So he went back home and married his sweetheart, Sally, and they got along well enough for the rest of their lives.

News

A rich landowner was returning home from a journey when he met by the side of the road the steward he had left in charge of his estate while he was away.

'Ah, steward,' hailed the returning gentleman cheerily, 'how are you, old fellow? And how are things at home?'

'Bad enough, sir,' said the steward. 'The magpie is dead.'

'Well, well,' said the gentleman. 'Poor magpie. Gone at last, eh? And how did he die?'

'Over-ate himself, sir.'

'Did he indeed! The greedy bird! What was it he liked so much?'

'Horseflesh. That's what got him, sir. Horseflesh.'

'Never!' said the landowner. 'How ever did he manage to find so much horseflesh that it killed him?'

'All your father's horses, sir.'

'What! My father's horses! Are they dead too?'

'Aye, sir. Died of overwork.'

'Why ever should they be overworked, steward?'

'Carrying all that water, sir.'

'Carrying water! What were they carrying water for, man?'

'For sure, sir, to put the fire out.'

'Fire! What fire?'

'Why, sir, the fire that burned your father's house to the ground.'

'Good Lord, steward, is my father's house burnt down? How did that happen?'

'I reckon it were the torches, sir.'

'What torches?'

'Them we used at your mother's funeral, sir.'

'My mother is dead?'

'Aye, poor lady. She never looked up after it.'

'After what, man, after what?'

'The loss of your father, sir.'

'My father? Dead too?'

'Yes, poor gentleman. Took to his bed as soon as he heard of it.'

'Heard of what?'

'Of the bad news, sir.'

'More bad news! What bad news?'

'Well, sir, your bank has failed and all your money is lost, and you're not worth a penny in the world, sir. I thought I'd come and wait on you to tell you about it, sir, for I thought you'd like to hear the news.'

Pig Tale, One

A little boy went to stay with relatives in the country for his holiday. The relatives lived on a farm and the boy enjoyed himself no end, seeing things he'd never seen before.

When he got back home, he told his mother all about it. But one thing had impressed him very much, and that was a pig with its young ones.

'What did the pig do?' his mother asked.

'Oh, the little ones chased it,' said the boy, 'and when they caught it they knocked it down on its back and started pulling the buttons off its waistcoat.'

Pig Tale, Two

A few years back a fellow lived at Hogbourn in Berkshire called Bob Appleford. He was a pig-dealer by trade and a well-known character in those parts.

One day Bob started a rumour that he was keeping a prime fat pig at Hogbourn which he had a mind to give away as a reward to any man who could prove that he had *always strictly minded his own business*.

For a long time nobody came to try. Then the one or two who did try failed the test straightaway.

Meanwhile, over at Didcot a man was being egged on by his neighbours to claim the pig. He was a taciturn chap, never had much to do with anybody. In the end, he let himself be persuaded and went one morning to Bob Appleford's pig-yard.

'I be the man who minds my own business,' he said to Bob when they met, 'and I be come to get that pig.'

'I be glad to see 'e, then,' said Bob. 'Come and look at un.'

They went to the sty where the celebrated pig was, and both of them stood for a while admiring the animal.

Then Bob stroked the pig and remarked, 'It be a fine un, just as I said afore, b'ain't it?'

'Yes, it be,' said the Didcot claimant, 'surely a remarkable fine pig. And might I ask,' he went on, 'what 'e fed it on to make . . .'

'That be my business, not yours,' said Bob, interrupting. 'Good morning.'

Nobody else tried to claim the pig after that.

The Dauntless Lass

There was a young servant-girl who feared nothing—a dauntless lass, and a pretty one too. She lived with a farmer, and he and his friends were drinking one night when they ran out of beer.

'Never you mind,' the farmer said. 'My girl will go down to the pub and bring us some bottles back.'

Now the night was dark, pitch-black, unlit by moon or stars.

'Surely the lass will be afeared to go out such a dark night by herself all alone,' said the farmer's friends.

'Never!' said the farmer. 'She's afeared of nothing that's alive or dead.'

The girl went and returned with the beer, and the farmer's friends said it was a rare thing, a girl like her being so bold.

'That's nothing at all,' said the farmer. 'I tell you she'd go anywhere, day or night, for she's afeared of nothing that's alive or dead.'

There and then he offered to bet five pounds that none of his friends could name a thing the lass would be afraid to do.

One of the friends took on the bet, and they all agreed to meet next week on the same day, when the girl would be set a task.

Meanwhile, the friend who had made the bet went to the parson and borrowed the keys of the church. Then he went to the old sexton and struck a bargain. For a couple of pounds the sexton was to go into the church and hide himself in the charnel-house among the coffins and bones; and there he was to wait till the servant-girl came, when he was to frighten her.

The next week the farmer and his friends met as before.

'This is what your lass *won't* do,' said the friend who had made the bet. 'She *won't* go into the church alone at midnight and into the dead house and bring back a skull-bone.'

The farmer called the girl and told her he wanted her to go to the charnel-house and bring him back a skull. Without a word, off she went, to the amazement of the farmer's friends.

The lass let herself into the church and went to the charnel-house, feeling not a flicker of fear, where she picked up a skull from among the bodies and bones.

The old sexton was waiting, hidden behind the door, and he muffled out:

'Let that be, that's my mother's skull-bone.'

The dauntless lass put down the skull and picked up another.

'Let that be, that's my father's skull-bone,' moaned the sexton.

The girl put that one down and picked up another, and said aloud as she did so, for she had lost her temper now:

'Father or mother, sister or brother, I *must* have a skull-bone and that's my last word.'

At that she walked off with the skull and locked the door of the dead house behind her.

When she got home she put the skull on the table and said:

'There's the skull, master.'

'Didn't you hear nothing, Mary?' said the friend who had made the bet.

'Yes,' she said. 'Some fool of a ghost called out to me, "Let be, that's my father's skull-bone" and "Let be, that's my mother's skull-bone", but I told him straight that father's or mother's, sister's or brother's, I *must* have a skull-bone, so I took it and here it be, and as I was going I locked the door and I heard that ghost hollering and shrieking like mad.'

The friend who had made the bet jumped up and went like a shot from a gun. He knew just who it was had been hollering. And sure enough when he opened the door of the charnel-house, there was the old sexton in a dead faint from fright.

The farmer claimed the five pounds and gave them to the dauntless lass for her courage.

A while after this a squire from down in Suffolk buried his old mother. But the old lady would not rest. She kept coming into the house, especially at mealtimes. Sometimes you could see all of her, sometimes not all, and sometimes you could only see the knife and fork rise off the table and play about where her hands would be. This so much distressed the servants that they gave notice and quit; so the squire was left on his own and not knowing what to do.

One day he heard of the dauntless lass who was afraid of nothing and lived a few villages away in Norfolk. So he rode over and told her all about his mother and her ghost and asked the girl if she would come and work for him.

Ghosts meant nothing to her, the girl told the squire; she paid them no regard. But in the circumstances she thought this ought to be remembered in her wages. The squire was only too glad to agree, engaged her at a good wage, and she rode back with him to his house.

The first thing the girl did was always to lay a place for the ghost at meals; but she took great care not to put the knife and fork criss-cross on the table—for that is a powerful protector from ghosts. And at meals she would hand the vegetables to the ghost, and do everything else just as if the ghost was no ghost at all but the squire's mother alive.

'Pepper, mum,' she'd say as she passed the pot, and, 'Salt, mum,' as she passed the salt dish.

Sure enough this seemed to please the old ghost no end. But nothing came of it till the squire had to go up to London on business.

Next day, when the squire was gone, the dauntless lass was on her knees cleaning the parlour grate when she noticed a thin shape push through the door, which was just ajar, and when it got through into the room it turned out to be the old mother's ghost.

'Mary, are you afeared of me?' asked the ghost.

'No, mum,' said the girl. 'I've no call to be afeared of you, for *you* be dead, and *I'm* alive.'

That flummoxed the old ghost for a minute. But then she went on:

'Mary, you come down the cellar with me—and don't bring a light for I'll shine enough for you to see.'

So down they went, down the cellar steps with the old ghost shining like a lantern, and when they reached the bottom the ghost pointed at some loose tiles in the floor and said:

'Pick you up those tiles, Mary.'

The girl did as she was bidden, and there, under the tiles, were two bags of gold, one big one and one little one.

'Now, Mary,' said the ghost, 'that big bag is for your master, and that little bag is for you, for you're a fearless lass and deserve it.'

With that the ghost vanished and the light she gave off along with her, so the girl had to grope her way back up the steps in the dark.

In three days' time, back again came the squire.

'Have you seen anything of my mother's ghost since I've been away, Mary?' he said.

'Yes, sir,' the girl replied, 'I have, and if you aren't afeared of coming down the cellar with me, I'll show you something.'

The squire laughed, and said *he* wasn't afraid if *she* wasn't—for the dauntless lass was a very pretty lass too!

So they lit a candle and went down, and the girl opened up the tiles.

'There are two bags of gold there, master,' she said. 'The *little* one is for you, and the big one is for *me*.'

'Lor!' said the squire, and thought that his mother might have left him, her own son, the big bag—but he took what he could nonetheless.

Ever after, when she laid the table, the girl always crossed the knives and forks, and so she kept the ghost from telling what she had done.

The squire, however, thought everything over in his mind, and after a while he up and married the dauntless lass, so this way he got both bags of gold after all. And he used to beat the girl whenever he got drunk, which was often. Aye, and she maybe deserved it for deceiving the old ghost.

A Day at the Seaside

An old countrywoman went to the seaside for the first time in her life. Before she set off, her neighbour told her to be sure and bring back a nice bottle of sea water for a souvenir. So when the old woman got to the shore, the tide was in, and she asked an old boatman if he would sell her a bottle of sea water.

The old boatman looked at her for a minute and said, 'You can fill your bottle for fivepence.'

The old woman gave him the money and filled her bottle

and went away to look round the town.

Some time later she came back for a last look at the sea before going home. By now the tide was out.

'My word,' said the old woman to the boatman. 'You have done a good trade!'

What the Devil

An amateur dramatic society in Suffolk was putting on a play and John Adroyns was acting the part of the Devil. When the performance was over, John set off for home, which was in a village a couple of miles out of town. But he didn't have a change of clothes, so off he went still dressed in his Devil's costume, with horns on his head, black tights on his legs, a black cloak flung over his shoulders and a forked tail trailing the ground behind.

On his way John had to pass by a rabbit warren kept by a gentleman who lived in his village. And just at the moment when he came walking along towards it, a couple of poachers were busy with a net and a ferret, catching rabbits. They had just sent the ferret down a hole and had covered the rabbits' exit with the net when they caught sight of John. His cloak billowed behind him, and his Devil's shape silhouetted against the moonlit sky was far more convincing than it had been on stage. When the poachers saw him bearing down upon them, they took him for the Devil himself, let out one yelp of terror and fled off down the road.

John, for his part, did not see the poachers' abandoned net lying across his path. His gaze was fixed with surprise on the retreating figures of the two men he had unexpectedly flushed from his feet like a brace of partridge. And not seeing it lying there, he stumbled into the net's enmeshing folds and fell down with a crack near sharp enough to break his neck.

Only when he had recovered from his fall did John find it was a poacher's net that had tripped him. At once he guessed what the men had been up to. And when he scrambled to his feet, he saw a horse tethered by the roadside hedge, its back laden with poached coneys. So he gathered up the net, mounted the horse and rode off to the house of the gentleman who owned the warren. He hoped to get the owner's thanks for his services and maybe a rabbit or two by way of reward.

Arrived there, he knocked at the door. One of the gentleman's servants opened it. But he took one look at John Adroyns dressed in his Devil's costume standing horned and evil-black in the moonlight and slammed the door with fright. Nor did he pause to think, but scurried off to his master, to whom, through a fit of the shakes, he managed to stammer out the message that the Devil was at the door.

The gentleman thought his servant had gone mad; or maybe had been tippling the wine in the cellar again. At any rate, another servant was sent to see who was standing outside. This fellow could not bring himself to open the door. He, at least, thought there might be more truth in his companion's words than either madness or wine. So he called out, 'Who's there?'

John Adroyns replied, 'Tell your master I must speak to him for a minute before I go.'

My goodness, it *is* the Devil! thought the servant, who hurried back to his master and said, 'Sure enough, sir, it is the Devil out there, and he says he wants a word with you before he'll go.'

'Fool!' said the gentleman. 'Oaf! Get my steward. He's the only one among you with any sense. Send him to have a look at this chap.'

The steward, when he got to the door, didn't open it and he didn't say anything either. Instead, he peeped through the keyhole. Squinting one way, he caught a glimpse of John's horns; squinting another way, he saw his tail.

By heaven, he thought, it's Old Nick himself sure enough! And I'll bet he's after taking the lot of us to hell, myself and all!

He hurried back to his master.

'It's the Devil out there, sir, no doubt about it. I saw his horns and tail with my own eyes,' he said, his face now white as whey.

'What! You too!' bellowed the gentleman, struggling out of his chair by the fire. 'I suppose I shall have to look for myself.'

Followed by his steward and the two servants, he shuffled off in his carpet slippers to the front door. There he paused, his hand on the latch.

'Better take a glimmer first,' he said, and bent his eye to the keyhole.

By this time, John Adroyns had grown tired of standing in the cold, and had mounted the horse again, ready to ride off home if the master of the house refused to see him that night.

So when the gentleman peered out what he saw was a horned black figure ringed by the moon and seated upon a frost-white horse hung about with lifeless shapes.

'Lord save us, you were right, steward!' whispered the gentleman. 'The Devil it is, seated on a horse laden with the souls of children! Now listen,' he went on, his head still bent to the keyhole. 'I'll keep an eye on him. You nip off and bring back my shot gun. We'll give Old Nick sommat to remember us by, eh?'

Off went the steward to the gun room, and back he came with his master's favourite fowling piece, ready loaded.

'Now,' said the gentleman, taking the weapon. 'When I give the word, open the door a crack, and I'll let fly. And remember, men, don't let him set eyes on you or you're done for.'

The two servants stood back out of the way. The steward prepared himself to pull the door ajar. The gentleman knelt and poised his gun for action.

'Now!' he said.

The door was opened.

The gun was pointed through the gap.

There was an ear-splitting explosion.

The door was shut again.

It was a few moments before anyone standing in the hall could hear clearly again. When they could, there was nothing but the sound of a horse's hooves pounding away into the distance and from the ground in front of the door came a small and trembling voice:

'Hold your fire! Hold your fire! It is I, John Adroyns. Your neighbour from the village. Hold your fire!'

'John Adroyns!' said the gentleman.

'For certain, it sounds like him, sir,' said the steward.

'Are you not the Devil then?' shouted the master.

'The Devil!' called back John. 'Why no. I'm your neighbour, John Adroyns. I was acting the Devil in a play, that's all. And on my way home tonight I came across poachers stealing from your warren. I was bringing you their horse and the rabbits they'd taken.'

By now there was no doubt who this devil was. The gentleman flung open the door and rushed out. There was John, spreadeagled in the mud, where he had been flung when the gunshot startled his horse, which went galloping off.

Master and servants hoisted John to his feet and helped him inside. There they assured themselves he was unharmed in all but shaken nerves, revived him with a glass of rum, set him comfortably by the glowing fire, and gentleman, guest and servants had a good laugh together at the whole ridiculous escapade.

Work Horse

A bricklayer was building a house, and the lad he had for carrying up his bricks was very slow; he only managed about two or three bricks at a time.

In the end the bricklayer got fed up with this, so one day he said to the lad, 'Look, matey, I'm going to tell you how it is. If you don't fetch more bricks up at a time and move a bit faster, then you can just pack up and go and I'll get somebody else to carry me hod.'

'All right,' said the lad. 'I'll see if I can do better.'

'You want to bring about a couple of dozen at a time,' said the bricklayer.

The lad didn't reply, just looked at him for a minute before going off to work again.

Next time the brickie saw the lad, he was half way up the ladder with a hod full of bricks on his back. But that wasn't all. The strange part was that he had a tail hanging from his backside.

'Hey!' shouted the bricklayer. 'What's trouble now? What you wearing that thing for?'

The lad shouted back, 'If I have to work like a blinkin' horse, I might as well be one.'

The Contrairy Wife

A farmer was brought to court accused of murdering his wife. The trial had been going on a whole day when the farmer said:

'It's about time I was away home for my dinner. But before I go, you'd maybe like to know how it happened.'

'Good heavens, man, that's what we've been wanting to know all day,' said the judge.

'Well,' said the farmer, 'it was like this. My wife was a contrairy woman. Always had to be opposite to everybody else. And she was getting up late one Sunday morning, so I said, "We'll not go to church this morning. It's getten too late."

'"Yes, we will," she says. "Get yourself ready and we'll be off."

'So when we set off, I said, "Shall we go by nearest road?"

'"No," she says, "we'll go t'other way."

'So we went the way she wanted, till we had to cross a rickety wooden bridge and I says to her, "I'll go first and see if it's safe."

'She says, "No you won't. I'll go first."

'Well, she gets half way over and down she goes, into the river. I thought to myself, she's bound to be contrairy still. So I run up the river—against the stream like, you see. But, dang me, she was that jolly contrairy she went t'other way after all. And so when I went chasing down stream to find her, and got her out, she was dead. She was contrairy all her life. And she were contrairy when she died.'

The Twins

There were two brothers who were identical twins. Sometimes even their own mother had to study them hard before she could tell t'other from which. Anyway, when they got to school age, they were sent off to different schools so that nobody would have trouble mixing them up, you see.

Both lads turned out to be quite bright, clever chaps who learned their lessons easily. Trouble was, the teacher of one of them didn't care much for him and was always looking for a chance to bring the lad down a peg or two.

Well, one year, after the exams, this brother got better marks than anybody else, and a lot better than the teacher wanted him to have.

'Before I'll let you be top of the class,' said the teacher, 'you'll have to answer me three questions. You can have till tomorrow morning to think about them. The questions are: What is the weight of the moon? What is the depth of the sea? And, last, what am I thinking?'

The lad went off home and that night he wouldn't play with his brother because he was puzzling over the answers to the teacher's questions. In the finish, his brother asked him why he was so long in the face.

'Teacher's given me three questions before he'll let me be top of the class and I can't think of the answers,' he said.

'What're the questions?' his brother asked.

When he told them, his brother said, 'Never mind about the questions. Just you let me go to your school tomorrow instead of you, and you go to mine. Our mates will tell us where to sit.'

So in the morning both brothers went to each other's schools. And after a bit, the teacher told the twin to stand up.

'Now,' he said, 'what about my questions? What weight is the moon?'

'A hundredweight, sir,' said the lad.

'How do you make that out?'

'Well, sir, there's four quarters in a hundredweight and four quarters in the moon.'

'Very good,' said the teacher. 'And what do you think is the depth of the sea?'

'A stone's throw, sir.'

'Why's that?'

'When you throw a stone it goes straight to the bottom, sir.'

'Well done,' said the teacher. 'Now for the third and hardest question. What am I thinking?'

'Please, sir,' said the lad, 'you're thinking I'm our Bobby, but I'm not. I'm his brother, Tommy.'

Miles Per Cow

A stranger was walking from Stroud to Cirencester. After plodding up Chalford Hill, he felt puffed and wondered how much further he had to go. Just then a farmer came by, walking the other way.

'How far to Cirencester?' asked the stranger.

'With a cow or without a cow?' replied the farmer.

'Without a cow, I suppose,' said the stranger.

'I can't tell 'e, then,' said the farmer. 'I never done it without a cow.'

The Gaffers of Gotham

They used to say that Gotham in Nottinghamshire was a village full of funny folk. Maybe it was; though likely they were no dafter than people in other places. Anyway, there are all sorts of tales told about them, and these are two.

The Rolling Cheeses

A man from Gotham made tasty round cheeses, and to get the best price he could for them he always went to Nottingham market and sold them there. It was a canny walk and used to tire him out, lugging all those cheeses that far. One day, however, he was on his way to market and had just reached the top of the hill that sweeps down into town, when one of his cheeses fell out of his bag and rolled off down the road.

'Hello,' he said, 'so you can run to market on your own, can you? Why should I bother to carry the rest of you, then?'

So he took off his bag and laid it down on the road, took out the rest of the cheeses, and one after the other sent them rolling down the hill. Some swerved into the bushes at the sides of the road, others bounced off towards the town.

'Now mind,' shouted their owner after them, 'make sure you go straight to market. I'll meet you there.'

Pleased that he'd have an easier walk the rest of the way, he set off happily and was soon down the hill, across the bridge over the River Trent at the bottom, and on into the market. When he got there, he searched everywhere among the stalls for his cheeses but couldn't find a sign of them. So he button-holed a friend of his.

'Have you seen my cheeses?' he asked.

'I haven't,' said his friend. 'Who was fetching them for you?'

'Nobody,' said the man. 'They were fetching themselves. They know their way well enough.'

'Is that right? Fetching themselves, eh?' said his friend, but said no more, for he knew all about folk from Gotham.

'Devil take them!' said the man. 'I know what's up. They ran off so fast, they've gone right past market. They must be near into York by now! I'd best chase after them.'

And away he went to hire a horse and ride to York, where he pestered everybody he met about his lost cheeses. But nobody had seen them.

Counting the Drowned

Twelve men of Gotham went fishing one day. Some of them stood on the bank and cast their lines from there; others waded waist deep in the water and fished from there. Now the River Trent is dangerous in places, even folk from Gotham knew that. And on the way home at the end of the day one of the men said, 'We took a risk, lads, plodging about in the river like that. I hope none of us is drowned.'

'My Lord, he's right!' said another of the party. 'We'd best see about it. Twelve of us came out this morning. Let's count and see that twelve are going back.'

So each man in turn counted his friends. But each man forgot to count himself.

'There's only eleven of us now,' said one after the other as each finished totting up. 'God help us, one of us is drowned!'

At once they turned about and went back to the riverside where they had been fishing, and looked up stream and down for the man who was lost, and all the time they moaned and shook their heads and wrung their hands with grief.

While they were standing there lamenting their sorry fate, a stranger came riding by. Seeing the distressed men of Gotham, he stopped and asked what was the matter.

'Why, sir,' said one of them, 'we came here to fish this morning and there were twelve of us then. Now one is drowned, and we're only eleven.'

The stranger looked at the mournful group for a moment before he said, 'Count yourselves again, gentlemen, if you will.'

One of the men obliged; but once more he counted his eleven companions and missed himself.

'You see, sir,' he said. 'Eleven of what was twelve.'

'Well, well!' said the stranger. 'How much will you give me if I find the twelfth man?'

'Sir,' said the men of Gotham with gratitude, 'we'll give you all the money we have with us.'

'Give me the money,' said the stranger.

Everyone in the party turned out his pockets; before long the stranger had collected a tidy sum.

'Now, let me see,' he said. And with that he whacked the first man of Gotham a hefty thump on his shoulder that brought stars to the poor fellow's eyes and a groan at the weight of the blow.

'There is one,' said the stranger, and gave the second man a similar thump before the first had begun to recover. And so he quickly went on, giving a resounding thwack to each and every man, counting as he went.

'And here,' he said as he reached the last, 'is the twelfth man.'

'Why, God bless you, sir,' said the men of Gotham when they'd sufficiently recovered breath to speak. 'What a marvel you are. You've found our neighbour we thought was lost!'

And they went home rejoicing.

The Tramp and the Rich Man

A tramp came begging at a rich man's door. The poor fellow was foul smelling, ugly to look at and altogether in a bad way. When the rich man came to the door, his nose twitched, he took a step backward, and he waved the tramp away.

'Get off with you,' he said. 'You look as if you've just come out of hell.'

The tramp could see he wasn't likely to be given one penny to put on another, so he said:

'Sure, sir, you've said the truth. I do indeed come straight out of hell.'

'Why didn't you stay there, then,' said the rich man, 'instead of coming here to bother me?'

'Why, sir,' said the tramp, 'there's no room down there for poor beggars like me. The whole place is kept for such gentlemen as yourself.'

Nuts

There was a man who loved nuts. So he planted hazel and filbert trees in his orchard and cherished them carefully all his life. When he died, he left orders in his will that a sack of nuts must be buried with him; and this was done.

The night after he was buried a miller was passing the man's orchard on his way home from work. He was still dressed in his white overalls and his face and hair were covered in flour-dust. As he walked by the orchard he thought how much he'd like to have some of the dead man's nuts. So he climbed over the wall into the orchard. No sooner had his feet touched ground than a black figure appeared from behind a nut tree in front of him.

The miller yelped in fright.

'Hold on, mate,' said the black figure in a whisper. ''Tis only me.'

The miller looked closely at the other man and saw by the thin moonlight that it was no one worse than his best friend, the tailor, dressed in the dark suit of his trade.

'What you doing, man?' asked the miller. 'You scared the life out of me.'

'I'm after stealing one of the old boy's sheep. What about you?' said the tailor.

'I thowt I'd help meself to a few of his nuts.'

'You old devil!' said the tailor nudging his friend.

'You old villain!' said the miller, nudging him back.

And they had a good chuckle together.

When they'd sobered up again, they agreed that each should do his job and then meet afterwards in the church porch. So off they went.

The miller had filled his pockets with nuts and arrived at the church before the tailor. So he sat himself in the porch and settled himself to await his pal, cracking himself a nut or two the while.

It happened that just then the sexton came along to lock up the church. As he came up the path he heard the noise of the miller cracking nuts and, wondering whatever it could be, he crept stealthily up to the church porch until, by the glim of the moon, he could dimly see inside. There he saw a figure all in white knakking nuts.

'By God,' he thought, ''tis the old gent we buried yesterday rose from his grave and feeding on his sack of nuts!'

Without a second glance, the terrified sexton ran off as fast as his trembling legs could carry him to tell his lodger at home what he had seen.

Now the lodger, poor fellow, was crippled with the gout and not, that night, in a happy mood. When the sexton rushed in all of a flutter, disturbing his peace with a gabbled tale about ghosts knakking nuts, the lodger wasn't best pleased.

'Man, you're a ninny,' he said. 'Ghosts, my swollen foot! If I could, I'd go up to the church myself and soon deal with your nut-scoffing spook.'

'Well, then,' said the sexton, 'if you dare go, I'll carry you there on my back, for I tell you that ghost looked real enough to me.'

The lodger grumbled a minute or two and gave the sexton a few sharp looks, but his bluff had been called and he couldn't wriggle out of it. In the end, he clambered on to the sexton's back and off the pair staggered.

As they approached the church up the graveyard path, the miller saw them coming. But all he could make out in the gloom was a humped figure bearing something on its back. Of course, he supposed this was the tailor with his rustled sheep. So he got up and went to meet him, calling cheerily:

'Is he fat? Is he fat?'

Sexton, seeing the white shape coming towards him, and hearing the miller's question, was scared out of his jittery wits.

'Fat or lean, you take him, if you want him,' he called back, and without another word, he threw the lodger to the ground and ran off like greased lightning.

The lodger, for his part, suddenly found himself not only able to stand, which he did just as soon as he touched ground, but miraculously able to run too. Gout or no gout, he took off after the sexton and fled, quick as a hare.

The startled miller could hardly make out what was happening. As far as he could tell, there seemed to be two men, one chasing the other. He guessed, therefore, that someone had spied the tailor stealing the sheep, had come after him, had all but caught him in the churchyard, and that the tailor had escaped again in the nick of time.

The miller's next thought gave him a start. What if someone had seen him, too, stealing the nuts? And what if at that very second they were watching from the shadows ready to pounce? He decided to hang about no longer, but crept off home there and then.

The miller had left the churchyard only a few minutes before his pal turned up at last, his stolen sheep slung across his shoulders. When the tailor couldn't find the miller, he supposed his friend had been and gone home – as indeed he had! So the tailor hitched the sheep to a more comfortable place on his back and set off in the direction of the miller's house, for he was determined to show his prize to his friend.

Meanwhile, the panicky sexton, all a-dither, fled to the vicarage, where he panted out his tale of a nut-cracking corpse risen from the dead. The vicar tried his best to calm the fellow. But in the end he had to agree to go to the churchyard with the sexton, and there lay the spectre. So, donned in surplice and stole, the vicar set off with his sexton to do his holy duty.

It was just as the vicar and sexton turned into the churchyard that they met the tailor, laden with his burden, on the way out.

Thinking the vicar in his white surplice was the miller in his overall, the tailor said as he approached:

'By God, I have him! I have him!'

He meant, of course, his stolen sheep.

The vicar, peering into the dark, took the black shape of the tailor with a white thing over his shoulders to be the Devil bearing away the spirit of the dead man. At that, the minister quite forgot his sacred duty and ran off as fast as his cluttering robes would allow. Close on his heels came the sexton, driven well-nigh hysterical by this latest encounter.

Hello, thought the tailor as he watched the white figure racing away with a dark figure chasing after, someone was lying in wait for my pal. I'd best go to his help.

By the time he reached the miller's door, he was properly winded, could hardly catch his breath, for the sheep was a heavy load on his back and a hindrance to running. But he banged as vigorously as he could on the miller's door and heard his friend shout:

'Who's there?'

'Caught one,' shouted back the tailor between puffs. 'Got him fast . . . *puff, puff* . . . Tied by the legs.'

Drat it! thought the miller when he heard this. 'Tis the constable. He's caught the tailor, got him tied by the legs, and now he's after me. I'm off.

He opened the back door and sped into the night.

By chance, the vicar and sexton had arrived by the miller's house a few minutes before the tailor and were hiding in an angle of the building. Seeing again the tailor with the white sheep on his shoulders, they thought the Devil had pursued them. So they took to their heels once more. But not knowing the place well, the vicar slipped and tumbled head first into a river that flowed nearby.

'Help! Help!' he cried when he surfaced. 'Help!'

The tailor, standing at the miller's door, saw the miller making off in one direction, the sexton in another, and heard the vicar's voice crying out from the river.

'Tis the constable, he thought. And he's shouting for help from the party of men he's brought with him to nab me for stealing this sheep and the miller for pinching the nuts. I'm off.

At which, he dumped the heavy carcass of the sheep on the miller's doorstep, so as not to be delayed in his escape, and sprinted off.

All of which goes to show what folly it is to fear anything without just cause.

Start and Finish

Years ago there were two farmers whose farms lay next to each other. Both of the men had married about the same time and, as they were strict Baptists, when their sons were born one was called Alpha and the other one Omega. The two lads grew up together and were good friends. For a long time people called them 'The Beginning and the End', until a rich bookmaker, who was staying at the Ship on a fishing holiday, started calling them Start and Finish, and these names stuck to them for the rest of their lives.

When their fathers died the two lads took over the farms and, until they were old men, stayed good friends. Then one day Start, when he called on his old friend, stopped to look at what lay in the swill-tub which was standing outside the kitchen door of the farmhouse. As he stood gazing into the tub, and sniffing the smell of sour milk, cabbage water, and fermenting potato peelings, the old billy-goat, which had the run of the yard, seeing a target bent over by the tub, backed a few paces, and then charged, scoring such a good hit that Start ended up by sitting in the swill. Just then Finish came round the corner to see what all the row was about, and he was so tickled to see Start floundering about in the swill that he burst out laughing. This put Start into such a flaming temper that he scrambled out of the tub, and started a free-for-all, with Billy getting a butt in whenever he got the chance.

Well, next market day Start called on his lawyers and told them to bring Finish into court to get damages from him for battery and assault. Later in the day Finish came along to the same lawyers, and told them to do the same thing to Start. The lawyer chap explained that he couldn't act for two clients and, as Start had been there first, he'd give Finish a letter to take to another lawyer who, he thought, was even better at squeezing money out of people than he was himself.

So Finish set off with the note but, thinking that talking to a lawyer would be thirsty work, he called in at the Lamb and drank a couple of pints. Then he began to wonder if he wasn't a silly old fool to go to law, and by the time he'd swallowed a third pint, he decided life on a farm wasn't so bad if a chap kept on friendly terms with his neighbours. So he looked at the envelope he'd been given and saw that it had been held so long in his warm hand that the flap had come unstuck. He thought about things for a minute or two, then made up his mind and took out the letter and read:

Dear Fleecem,
Two old geese have come to market; you pluck one and I'll pluck the other.

Well, Finish got up from the table and wandered out into the street and walked along to the Sun, where he knew Start always put up his pony and trap. When he went into the inn he saw his old friend sitting alone at a table with a tankard in front of him. So Finish walked over to him and said:

'Just read that letter.'

Start read it, and then stood up and said:

'All right, let bygones be bygones; we'll shake hands and swallow a pint or two to soothe our ruffled feathers.'

And so they did, until the landlord told them it was time to finish up their drink and start for home, when they were in such a happy state that it took three men to lift them into the trap; and when they drove out of the yard the ostler said:

'Well, we've started them off but only they'll know where they'll finish.'

But the two old men got home all right, because Start's wife, who was sitting up waiting for him, found the pony trying to get into the stable, still hitched to the trap where the two bosom pals sat fast asleep.

A few days after this Start called on Finish and asked him if he'd like one of his fat geese for his Michaelmas dinner.

'That I would, bor,' said Finish.

'Well, you can have one, if you promise to save the feathers,' Start told him.

'I'll do that,' Finish promised him. 'Shall I bring them over to you, or will you come and fetch them?'

'Put them in a bag,' said Start, 'and bring them with you

when we go to market next week.'

So, on market day, the pair of them jogged along with two bags of feathers in the back of the trap. After stabling the pony and having a drink, the two men strolled down the street, each one carrying a bag of feathers. When they reached the first lawyer's office they began going upstairs, shaking those goose-feathers out of the bags as they went along, so by the time they got to the landing, the feathers were floating all over the place. There was a butcher's shop under the office and the butcher started swearing at the top of his voice when he saw his best joints all covered in fine goose down.

When the lawyer got back from his dinner he saw the feathers all along the stairs, so he dashed into his office and opened the windows. The draught sent the feathers swirling and flying about in the street till it looked like a snowstorm. Some of them settled on the stalls, and got all mixed up with rock and cockles, while a fishmonger roared out asking who in hell was going to buy fish covered with feathers instead of scales. While all this was going on, Start and Finish were watching through the windows of the Lamb; then, when everything was quiet again, they drove off home, laughing so much that people passing by said:

'There are those two old fools, drunk again.'

To Start and Finish the whole thing was a huge joke, but the trades-people made such a fuss that the police, after ferreting around, found out who'd played the trick and the two old chaps were taken before the magistrates, charged with a breach of the peace.

The court-room was packed when the case was heard. Start and Finish pleaded not guilty, and the justices' clerk, who turned out to be the other lawyer, Fleecem, asked what they had to say for themselves. The two men told him they understood that his lawyer friend sometimes did a bit of goose-plucking in his spare time and when the magistrate asked them what on earth they meant by that, Finish handed him that letter. Well, the magistrate read it out loud to the court and everybody roared with laughter till he told them to stop. Then he told Start and Finish that the case was dismissed and they could go; which they did. And they had a glorious booze-up in every pub in the town.

Coxhall Jobs

The people of Coggeshall (pronounced Coxhall) in Essex long ago acquired a reputation for foolishness. Hence the saying 'a Coxhall job' for any foolish act.

Among their reputed eccentricities are these:

Coggeshall folk once lit a fire under some plum trees in order to hasten the ripening of the fruit.

During a flood, an old woman sent for a carpenter and ordered him to pull down her staircase so that the flood waters wouldn't be able to climb up to her bedroom.

An enthusiastic fisherman, seeing the moon reflected in a pond, and being curious about what the moon was made of, tried to fish it out of the water with a rod and line.

When Coggeshall folk built their church they forgot to make any windows. So they got some large hampers, set them open in the sun to catch the light, then shut them up tight, wheeled them into the church in barrows, and there opened them again to let the light out.

Maybe, though, Coggeshall people are sharper than they're given credit for being. At any rate, it's said that one evening a stranger called at a Coggeshall public house.

'What be the name of this place, then?' he asked the landlord.

'This be Coxhall,' said the landlord.

'Oh, Coxhall is it!' said the stranger. 'That's where all the fools live, I do believe.'

'I don't know about that,' said the landlord. 'But we do get plenty passing through.'

Nor is Coggeshall the only place in England said to be full of fools. There are plenty more:

Aldbourne, Wilts	Haddenham, Bucks
Austwick, Yorks	Hadleigh, Suffolk
Benson, Oxon	Holderness, Humberside
Bolliton, Yorks	Idbury, Oxon
Borrowdale, Cumbria	Ilmington, Warwickshire
Bridlington, Humberside	Isle of Wight
Buckhampton, Wilts	Lambeth
Cambridge	Lavington, Wilts
Cannings, Wilts	Lincolnshire Fens
Chisledon, Wilts	Lorbottle, Northumberland
Claygate, Surrey	Middleton, Greater Manchester
Collingbourne, Wilts	Newbiggin, Roxburgh
Crewkerne, Somerset	Northleigh, Oxon
Darlaston, West Midlands	Pevensey, East Sussex
Dawley, Shropshire	Richmond, Yorks
Deanshanger, Northants	St Ives, Cornwall
Ebrinton, Glos	Settle, Yorks
Fimber, North Humberside	Shapwick, Dorset
Folkestone, Kent	Slaithwaite, Yorks
Gotham, Notts	Sutherland
Gornal, West Midlands	Tipton, West Midlands
Grendon, Northants	Whittingham Vale, Northumberlan

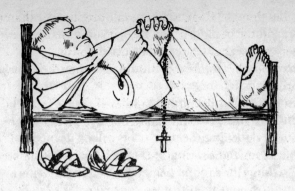

The Merry Monk

Long ago, in a Yorkshire town, there were two monasteries so close together that a single wall separated them. They were St Mary's Abbey and St Leonard's Priory.

Now one of the monks of St Leonard's was a fat jovial fellow named Brother Jucundus. All his life he had loved good food and plenty of it, and even more he loved good wine and plenty of it. How he had come, in middle age, to forsake his gay companions and enter a monastery, he never quite knew, but there he was, and after about a year of bread and vegetables, thin ale, and long prayers at midnight, daybreak and noon, he began to sigh for old times when he had lived on the fat of the land, had ridden to hounds and had helped himself to rich red wine whenever he had a mind to do so.

It was the custom of the brethren in St Leonard's to have a nap between one and two in the afternoon. One sunny day Brother Jucundus was alone in his cell, trying very hard to go to sleep but unable to do so because of the noise outside. There was the sound of many feet on the pavement. There was laughter. There was much shouting. He could hear music in the distance, and suddenly he realized that it was a fair day.

The fair! Brother Jucundus sat upright on his hard bed. The fair! There would be whirligigs and stalls and side-shows and dancing dogs and drinking booths. There would be fun and excitement. Brother Jucundus sighed as he looked at his bare feet and felt the stuff of his habit. Suddenly he decided that no matter what happened he *must* escape from his prison and share in the frivolity outside.

Stealthily opening the door of his cell he peeped out. All was still except for the snoring of some of the monks. He went on tiptoe to the Prior's room, helped himself to a silver crown from the alms-box, and then tiptoed to the Porter's lodge where he carefully laid hold of the keys, opened the outer door of the monastery and joined in the merry crowd hastening to the fair.

A happy man was Brother Jucundus that afternoon. He talked with everybody. He laughed till his fat body heaved again. He ate dozens of gingerbread horses. He saw the bearded woman. He went round and round on the whirligig, shouting like a schoolboy. He won a pocketful of nuts. He drank a long draught of ale; then another draught; then a third and after that a fourth, his red face becoming redder than ever. There was a see-saw, and Brother Jucundus climbed on rather unsteadily, two gay young men sitting at the other end. Down went the gay young men, and up went the merry monk, waving his arms and singing:

> '*In dulce jubilo*,
> Up, up, up we go!'

Then he looked down. For a moment the happy smile forsook his round face. There behind him stood two brethren from St Leonard's Priory, their faces stern, their eyes fixed upon him. But Brother Jucundus's happy smile returned. He waved to his brethren and invited them to join him. The see-saw came down with a bump, Brother Jucundus rolling off. Though quite unable to stand on his feet, he somehow managed to sing again:

> '*In dulce jubilo*,
> Down, down, down we go!'

Without a word the two monks who had been sent to look for their wayward brother picked him up, put him in a wheelbarrow, and conveyed him to the monastery. There the Prior and Chapter sat with severe and relentless countenances as the two brethren, who had searched all the afternoon, told how Brother Jucundus had been found on a see-saw. Plainly he had broken the rules of the Order. But they were fair to him.

'What have you to say in defence?' asked the Prior, shocked beyond measure.

Brother Jucundus beamed on his grim-visaged brethren as he lolled back in the wheelbarrow. '*In dulce jubilo* . . .' he began in his fine baritone.

It was enough. Brother Jucundus had brought disgrace on all, and it was unanimously agreed that he must suffer death for his crime. Solemnly, therefore, the monks left the Chapter House, four of them supporting Brother Jucundus along the stone-flagged court and down the steps leading to the wine cellar. Perhaps some inkling of what was going on began to dawn on the victim of the monks' righteous indignation, for, as the procession descended to the dim cellar, he began singing:

> '. . . down, down, down we go!'

They sat him on a stool in the corner of the cellar. They gave him a loaf of new bread and a cruse of water. Then some of the brethren brought stones and mortar, and gradually they walled him in. Brother Jucundus watched the mason monks at work, encouraged them with sly and good-natured remarks, and now and then broke into singing as he waved his hand to the Prior and the rest of the Chapter who were looking on with frowning faces. Long before the wall was raised to the level of Brother Jucundus's massive chest, he was sound asleep, but the work went on until the vaulted roof was reached, after which the Prior committed the soul of Brother Jucundus to the mercy of God, and then in company with the other monks left him to his fate.

A cruel fate it was, for Brother Jucundus was to starve to death slowly in his dark cold prison. Happily, however, he was at first unaware of this. He snored for some hours, and when at last he awoke he began struggling hard to free himself. He pushed and kicked. He threw himself this way and that. Suddenly he felt the wall behind him give way, and the next moment he tumbled backward amid an avalanche of stones and mortar.

For the life of him he could not tell where he was. Nothing he could see was familiar. He picked himself up, rubbed his shins, shook the mortar from his habit, and staggered painfully up the cellar steps and along corridors where thin-faced monks walked silently. Only after some hours did Brother Jucundus discover he had fallen out of St Leonard's Priory into St Mary's Abbey.

What is more, he had jumped out of the frying pan into the fire, for if life had been dull in St Leonard's, it was duller in St Mary's, where monks were sworn to utter silence, except on Easter Day. No one asked who he was, or where he had come from, the silent monks assuming that he was a novice, who had joined the monastery in the usual way. His bed was harder than the one he had had in St Leonard's. The food was coarser and there was less of it. The strict rules of the Order irked Brother Jucundus's jovial spirit sorely, but he could do no other than eat what was set before him, meditate on his sins and keep to the daily routine of prayers. For all that he lost the roundness of body and fulness of face that had been his in St Leonard's; and *how* he longed for the comfort he had once enjoyed!

Now it came to pass that after twelve months the Cellarer of St Mary's died, and that by a happy inspiration the Abbot appointed Brother Jucundus to that office. Thus it happened that when fair day came round again, Brother Jucundus, though unable to escape from St Mary's and go up and down on the see-saw once more, was able to slink down to the cellar and there help himself, not to the thin ale served daily to the monks, but to a cask of old malmsey kept for special guests. Brother Jucundus filled a mug with malmsey and drained it. He filled it again, and then again, and after that so many times he lost count, and was perfectly content to sit on the stone floor and draw off the malmsey as quickly as he could.

Meanwhile the monks waited in the refectory for their morning ration of ale. Their mugs remained empty. The silent fraternity dared not utter a word of protest, but they shuffled their feet under the tables, turned in their seats and mumbled among themselves. At last the Abbot could contain himself no longer. With long strides, his brow clouded, he marched off in the direction of the cellar, the rest of the monks, by common consent, following hard on his heels. Where was the Cellarer? No one knew, but all were determined to find out. Through the cloisters the angry monks hurried, down the steps, and so to the cellar, finding there a sight the like of which they had never seen before. Brother Jucundus lay on the floor, his head resting against a butt of their best malmsey, and as he waved his mug, he sang:

> '*In dulce jubilo*,
> Up, up, up we go!'

This was too flagrant an offence to be passed over, a sin too great for mercy. Abbot and monks considered the matter, there in the cellar, and with all speed. Though it was not Easter Day, the emergency provided them with an excuse for breaking silence, and by unanimous vote it was decided first to excommunicate Brother Jucundus with bell, book and candle, and then to wall him in the cellar, the scene of his crime, and leave him to die a lingering death.

No sooner was this said than it was done. There was a

convenient recess in one of the walls, indeed, a number of loose stones were actually to hand. Mortar was mixed, and one or two monks rolled up the sleeves of their habits and set to work to wall in Brother Jucundus. They gave him a loaf of fresh bread from the oven. They filled a cruse with water and put it by him. Within an hour the offending brother was lost to sight, and though they could still hear him singing the monks had no compunction in leaving him there to die.

Now Brother Jucundus was much too lively to know what was afoot, and so he kept singing:

> '*In dulce jubilo*,
> Up, up, up we go!'

as if he were enjoying all the fun of the fair. And he was still roaring forth as lustily as ever when, as it happened, the Cellarer of St Leonard's Priory went down to draw ale for the monks. He had filled a flagon and was about to carry it to the refectory when he stood as one turned to stone. The colour drained from his cheeks. The flagon dropped from his nerveless fingers. Someone was singing. He knew the voice. He recognized and remembered the words. Only one man had a voice like that. Only one could sing:

> '*In dulce jubilo*,
> Up, up, up we go!'

in just that utterly carefree manner. *He was Brother Jucundus!*

With something between terror and joy on his countenance the Cellarer rushed up the steps, calling aloud to the rest of the fraternity that Brother Jucundus was alive and singing. How the monks stared at him. They were slowly filing out of church, their faces even more grave than usual, for they had been to the recitation of Sext, and the office of the dead, their Prior having died only a few days before. At first they looked with contempt at the excited and flushed Cellarer. Poor fellow, perhaps in his grief for their dead Prior he had gone out of his mind? Or had he been drinking more than his own ration of ale? No doubt it was this last alarming thought which prompted the monks to turn from the refectory to the cloisters, following the agitated Cellarer down to the cellar, where, after a few minutes' silence, they were one and all astonished to hear someone singing:

'*In dulce jubilo*,
Up, up, up we go!'

It was a miracle. A year to the very day had Brother Jucundus been walled up in that narrow sepulchre, and yet here he was singing as merrily and lustily as ever!

For a moment not one of the monks could believe his ears. Then some ran off for chisels and pickaxes, and in next to no time they were hacking at the wall they had built twelve months before. Stone after stone was loosened; and, there, to the wonder and amazement of all, was Brother Jucundus, less corpulent than before, thinner in the face to be sure, but alive— alive after being walled up for a whole year! Even the loaf of bread was still warm. The cruse of water was untouched. It was a miracle indeed, and with one voice the brethren cried, 'Jucundus, our Prior! Jucundus, our head and father!'

So, carried up the steps on the shoulders of the admiring and joyful monks, Brother Jucundus was installed in the Prior's seat, and there he remained, jovial as ever, to the end of his days.

Last Word

Two old women were gossiping over their garden fence.

'You know Mrs Turner, used to live at number nineteen, and went to America with that flyer?'

'I know her well,' said the other.

'Well,' said the first, 'I hear tell she's dead.'

'Don't you believe it,' said her friend. 'I've heard nothing, and if it was true she'd have told me herself, for she writes to me about everything.'

The Drunken Clerk

Every year the vicar of Barthomley used to send a barrel of beer to the local colliery as a Christmas gift for the miners. One year he asked his parish clerk to transport the barrel for him.

On the way to the pit head, the clerk helped himself to a pint or two of the beer, which he enjoyed so much he gave himself a few more. By the time he reached the pit, the clerk was so drunk, he fell fast asleep in the bottom of the cart.

When the miners came up from their shift underground, they found the cart, and the half-empty barrel, and the drunken clerk snoring. So they thought to have their own back. Carefully, they lifted the clerk out of the cart and took him down the pit, where they left him.

After a couple of hours the clerk woke up. He opened his eyes and was horror-struck. He found himself lying in a dismal place, black as night, damp, stale, full of strange noises, and lit only by a few wandering lights carried by seemingly ugly beings that stumbled about in half-bent, ape-like fashion. As soon as he moved these creatures gathered round him, making chuckling sounds that scared the clerk even more.

What could it all mean? Had he died unawares? And was this the result?

Suddenly one of the strange creatures beside him said, 'Who are you? What's your name?'

In a trembling, submissive voice, the wayward clerk replied, 'When I was alive, sir, I was parish clerk at Barthomley. But any name you like to call me now will suit, good master Devil.'

Only when this was greeted with roars of laughter and a torrent of friendly banter did the wretched clerk begin to understand what had been done to him.

Three Old Men of Painswick

Oh! Painswick is a healthful town,
   It hath a bracing breeze,
Where men by nature's rules might live
   As long as e'er they please.

Before the glass and baneful pipe
   Had robb'd man of his strength,
And water only was his drink,
   He lived a greater length.

Two hundred years, or more, ago
   A pilgrim passed that way;
And what that pilgrim heard and saw
   I will relate today.

And while he stopp'd outside the town,
   To rest his weary bones,
He saw a very aged man
   Upon a heap of stones.

The pilgrim saw him with surprise,
   And surely thought he'd dream'd,
The poor man was so very old,
   Methuselah he seem'd!

He'd travelled o'er the wide, wide world
   Amid its heat and cold,
But he had never, never seen
   A man one half as old.

His face was wrinkled like a skin
   That's shrivelled by the heat;
His hair was whiter than the snow
   We tread beneath our feet.

It made the pilgrim very sad,
   As he was passing by,
To see his old eyes fill'd with tears,
   To hear him sob and cry.

The man was crying like a child,
   His tears fell like the rain,
The pilgrim felt for him, and ask'd,
   'Old man, are you in pain?

'Oh, tell me, tell me, poor old man,
   Why do you sob and cry?'
The old man rubbed his eyes and said,
   'Feethur's bin a b'yutting I.'

'Old man, old man, you must be mad,
    For that can never be;
Your father, surely, has been dead
    At least a century.'

'My feethur be alive and well,
    I wish that he weer dy'ud,
For he ha bin and byut his stick
    About my face and yud.'

The pilgrim pick'd the old man up,
    And walk'd to Painswick town;
'Oh, show me where your father lives,
    And I will put you down.

'And I will tell the cruel man
    Such things must not be done,
And I will say how wrong it is
    To beat his aged son.'

The pilgrim shook a garden gate,
    An old man ope'd the door;
His back was bended like a bow,
    His white beard swept the floor.

If Adam he had lived till now,
    And lengthen'd out his span,
Then Adam really would have seem'd
    Another such a man!

The pilgrim felt amazed, indeed,
    When he beheld his sire;
He held a great stick in his hand,
    His face was flushed with ire.

'Old man, old man, put down your stick,
    Why do you beat your son?'
'I'll cut the rascal to the quick,
    If he does what he've done.

'Why, up in yonder apple-tree
    Grandfather risked his bones;
And while the old man pick'd the fruit,
    The rascal dubb'd with stones.'

The pilgrim turn'd his head and saw,
    In a spreading apple-tree,
A very, very aged man,
    The eldest of the three.

The pilgrim was a holy man,
    Whose hopes were in the sky;
He fled—he thought it was a place
    Where man could never die!

Irish Stakes

An Englishman who loved driving his sports car very fast heard that in Ireland there were long roads, empty of traffic. So he took his car across to Ireland for a fortnight's holiday. Sure enough, he found plenty of empty roads. Day after day he enjoyed himself driving fast along them.

One day near the end of his holiday, he was driving down a long straight road. Sixty, seventy, eighty miles an hour he went, like the clappers, thrilled to bits with himself.

Suddenly, a tractor and trailer with two farmers sitting on it drove out of a field a hundred yards ahead. There was no time for the Englishman to stop. Thinking quickly, he spun the wheel, drove his car off the road, over the verge, into and out of a ditch, over a hedge, and into the field. Now he didn't dare stop, for his wheels would have sunk into the muddy ground. So he kept going like the clappers, fast as he could, down the field till he was beyond the tractor, then he bounced the car over the hedge, through the ditch, across the verge, on to the road again, and went off on his way, like the clappers, eighty miles an hour.

The two Irishmen watched the car's progress, eyes a-popping, until it disappeared in a cloud of dust down the road. Then one turned to the other and said, 'Did you see that, Paddy? Did you see that!'

'I did indeed,' said Paddy. 'Dangerous that!'

'Dangerous!' said the other. 'Why, man, we just got out of that field in time!'

Has Plummocks Legs?

One day two lads were scrumping damson plums from an orchard. One lad was up in the tree picking the plummocks and dropping them down to the other lad on the ground below. So fast were the plummocks coming that the lad on the ground was hard put to it to keep up. But he worked with a will, stuffing the fruit into his pockets, and every now and then hurriedly cramming a choice one into his mouth and swallowing it.

He had just bolted a particularly fat specimen when he stopped in his tracks and called up to his pal.

'Tom,' he said fearfully, 'has plummocks legs?'

'No,' replied his companion from the tree, not pausing in his work, ' 'course not.'

'Well then,' said the other grimly, 'I've just swallowed a frog.'

Too Clever by Half

A poor workman's son had been away at university for many years. At last he came home to visit his father and mother so the old folks bought two small chickens, the best they could afford, to have as a celebration for supper that night.

All day, the son kept boasting about how clever he was and showing off his knowledge. The parents listened patiently. Then, that night during supper, the two roast chickens were placed on the table, and the son said,

'I can prove to you, father, that by the rules of logic and arithmetic these two chickens are really three.'

'Can you now?' said the old man. 'Let's hear then.'

'Right,' said the son, very superior. He tapped one of the skinny fowl with his knife. 'This chicken is one. Correct?'

'Aye, it is,' said the father, not batting an eye.

'And this is two,' said the son, tapping the other bird. 'Well even you, father, know that one and two make three!'

'Very neat, that,' said the old man. 'I'll tell you what, son. Since you're that clever and know so much, your mother shall have the first chicken, I'll have the second, and the third you can keep for yourself.'

Table Manners

A man in a restaurant said to the waitress, 'I say, miss, you've got your thumb in my soup.'

'That's all right,' said the waitress. 'The soup ain't hot.'

Sir Gammer Vans

Last Sunday morning at six o'clock in the evening as I was sailing over the tops of the mountains in my little boat, I met two men on horseback riding on one mare: so I asked them, 'Could you tell me whether the old woman was dead yet who was hanged last Saturday week for drowning herself in a shower of feathers?' They said they could not positively inform me, but if I went to Sir Gammer Vans he could tell me all about it.

'But how am I to know the house?' said I.

'Ho, 'tis easy enough,' said they, 'for 'tis a brick house, built entirely of flints, standing alone by itself in the middle of sixty or seventy others just like it.'

'Oh, nothing in the world is easier,' said I.

'Nothing *can* be easier,' said they: so I went on my way.

Now this Sir G. Vans was a giant, and a bottle-maker. And as all giants who *are* bottle-makers usually pop out of a little

thumb-bottle from behind the door, so did Sir G. Vans.

'How d'ye do?' says he.

'Very well, I thank you,' says I.

So he gave me a slice of beer, and a cup of cold veal; and there was a little dog under the table that picked up all the crumbs.

'Hang him,' says I.

'No, don't hang him,' says he, 'for he killed a hare yesterday. And if you don't believe me, I'll show you the hare alive in a basket.'

So he took me into his garden to show the curiosities. In one corner there was a fox hatching eagle's eggs; in another there was an iron apple-tree, entirely covered with pears and lead; in the third there was the hare which the dog killed yesterday alive in the basket; and in the fourth there were twenty-four *hipper-switches* threshing tobacco, and at the sight of me they threshed so hard that they drove the plug through the wall, and through a little dog that was passing by on the other side. I, hearing the dog howl, jumped over the wall; and turned it as neatly inside out as possible, when it ran away as if it had not an hour to live. Then he took me into the park to show me his deer: and I remembered that I had a warrant in my pocket to shoot venison for his majesty's dinner. So I set fire to my bow, poised my arrow, and shot among them. I broke seventeen ribs on one side, and twenty-one and a half on the other; but my arrow passed clean through without ever touching it, and the worst was I lost my arrow: however, I found it again in the hollow of a tree. I felt it; it felt clammy. I smelt it; it smelt honey.

'Oh, ho,' said I, 'here's a bees' nest,' when out sprang a covey of partridges. I shot at them; some say I killed eighteen; but I am sure I killed thirty-six, besides a dead salmon which was flying over the bridge, of which I made the best apple-pie I ever tasted.

Know Me . . .

A man rushed into a Yorkshire police station at midnight.

'My wife,' he gasped. 'Will you find my wife? She's been missing since eight this evening. I must find her!'

'Particulars?' asked the sergeant. 'Height?'

'I—I don't know.'

'Do you know how she was dressed?'

'No, but I do know she took the dog with her.'

'What kind of dog?'

'Brindle bull terrier, weight 53 pounds, four dark blotches on his body shading from grey to white, three white legs, and right front leg brindled all but the toes. A small nick in his left ear.'

'That'll do,' gasped the sergeant. 'We'll find the dog!'

Just Good Lads

All through the night London police were combing the underworld for three youths who escaped over the wall from Wormwood Scrubs jail, London.

Mrs Johnson was picking blackberries on Wednesday afternoon when she saw a length of black rope thrown over the jail wall. A wooden ladder followed, and three men dropped on to the grass in the lane which divides Mrs Johnson's garden from the prison wall.

'I thought they were dodging out for a cup of tea, and intended to go back again,' said Mrs Johnson. 'I didn't bother to raise the alarm.'

Mr Pengelly, the Devil and a Tramp

Mr Pengelly was vicar of Morwenstow in Cornwall, a man so hard to get the better of that even the Devil couldn't manage it. He did try. It happened one night when Mr Pengelly was very ill and like to die. The Devil came to the side of his bed, and said to him:

'Mr Pengelly, I will trouble yu, if you please.'

'Yu will trouble me with what, your Honour?' says Mr Pengelly, sitting up in bed.

'Why just to step along of me, sir,' says the Devil.

'Oh, but I don't please at all,' says Mr Pengelly, lying down again, and tucking his pillow under his cheek.

'Well, sir, but time's up, yu know,' was the remark the Devil made thereupon; 'and whether it pleases yu or no, yu must come along of me at once, sir. It isn't much of a distance to speak of from Morwenstow,' says he, by way of apology.

'If I must go, sir,' says Mr Pengelly, wiping his nose with his blue pocket-handkerchief covered with white spots, and RP marked in the corner in red cotton, 'why then, I suppose yu ain't in a great hurry. Yu'll give me ten minutes?'

'What do'y want ten minutes for, Mr Pengelly?' asks the Devil.

'Why, sir,' says Mr Pengelly, putting his blue pocket-handkerchief over his face, 'I'm ashamed to name it, but I shud like to say my prayers. Leastwise, they cudn't do no harm,' exclaimed he, pulling the handkerchief off his face, and looking out.

'They wouldn't du yer no gude, Mr Pengelly,' says the Devil.

'I shud be more comfable in my mind, sir, if I said 'em,' says he.

'Now, I'll tell yu what, Mr Pengelly,' says the Devil, after a pause, 'I'd like to deal handsome by yu. Yu've donne many a gude turn in your day. I'll let yu live as long as yonder cann'l-end burns.'

'Thank'y kindly, sir,' says Mr Pengelly. And presently he says, for the Devil did not make sign of departing, 'Would yu be so civil as just tu step out into t'other room, sir? I'd take it civil. I can't pray comfably with yu here, sir.'

'I'll oblige yu in that too,' says the Devil, and he went to look after Mrs Pengelly.

No sooner was his back turned than Mr Pengelly jumped out of bed, extinguished the candle-end, clapped it in the candle-box, and put the candle-box under his bed.

Presently the Devil came in, and said, 'Now, Mr Pengelly, yu're in the dark, I see the cann'l's burnt out, so yu must come with me.'

'I'm not so much in the dark as yu, sir,' says the sick man, 'for the cann'l's not burnt out, and isn't like tu. He's safe in the cann'l-box. And I'll send for yu, sir, when I want yu.'

So the Devil went off in a dudgeon and it was many a year before he had another chance to cheat Mr Pengelly of his soul.

But there was a man who did manage to get the better of Mr Pengelly. He was a tramp and it happened this way:

One day a man in tatters, and with his shoes in fragments, came to his door and asked for work.

'I like work,' says the man. 'I love it. Try me.'

'If that's the case,' says Mr Pengelly, 'yu may dig my garden for me, and I will give yu one shilling and twopence a day.' Wages were then eighteen pence, or one and sixpence.

'Done,' says the man.

So he was given a spade, and he worked capitally. Mr Pengelly watched him from his windows, from behind a wall, and the man never left off work except to spit on his hands; that was his only relaxation, and he did not do that over often.

Mr Pengelly was mighty pleased with his workman; he sent him to sleep in the barn, and paid him his day's wage, that he might buy himself a bit of bread.

Next morning Mr Pengelly was up with the lark. But the workman was up before Mr Pengelly or the lark either, and was digging diligently in the garden.

Mr Pengelly was more and more pleased with his man. He went to him during the morning; then the fellow stuck his spade into the ground, and said, 'I'll tell yu what it is, sir; I

like work, I love it; but I cannot dig without butes or shoes.
Yu may look. I've no soles to my feet, and the spade nigh cuts
through them.'

'Yu must get a pair of shoes,' says Mr Pengelly.

'That's just it,' says the man, 'but no bootmaker will trust
me, and I cannot pay down, for I haven't the money, sir.'

'What would a pair of shoes cost now?' asks his employer,
looking at the man's feet, wholly devoid of leather soles.

'Fefteen shilling, maybe,' says he.

'Fefteen shilling!' exclaims Mr Pengelly. 'Yu'll never get
that to pay him.'

'Then I must go to some other farmer, who'll advance the
money,' says the man.

'Now dont'y be in no hurry,' says Mr Pengelly, in a fright
lest he should lose a man worth half-a-crown a day by his
work. 'Suppose I were to let'y have five shilling. Then yu
might go to Stratton, and pay that, and in five days yu would
have worked it out, keeping twopence a day for your meat;
and that will do nicely, if yu're not dainty. Then I would let'y
have another five shilling, till yu'd paid up.'

'Done,' says the man.

So Mr Pengelly pulled the five shillings out, in two half-
crown pieces, and gave them to the man.

Directly he had the money in his hand the fellow drove the
spade into the ground, and, making for the gate, took off his
hat, and said, 'I wish yu gude morning, Mr Pengelly. And
many thanks for the crown. Now I'm off to Taunton, like a
long dog.'

And like a long dog he went, and Mr Pengelly never saw
him or his two half-crowns again. So the man who cheated the
Devil was cheated by a tramp. That shows how clever tramps
are.

Marking the Spot

Two men went out fishing together on a lake in a hired boat. For a time they had no luck. But then they drifted to a spot where they caught one fish after another just as quickly as they could haul in their lines and cast them out again.

'Why, man,' said one to the other, 'this is the spot to come all right.'

'It is an' all,' said his friend. 'Let's be sure to come here again tomorrow.'

'Right,' said the first, 'make certain you've marked the place then.'

At the end of the day, when they had returned the boat to the owner and were on their way home, the first man said to his mate, 'Did you mark the spot like I told you?'

'I did,' replied the other. 'I cut a line with me knife on the side of the boat.'

'Why you daft fool,' said the first man. 'What good was that? They might give us a different boat tomorrow.'

The Barber's Clever Wife

Once upon a time there lived a barber, who was such a poor silly creature that he couldn't even ply his trade decently, but snipped off his customers' ears instead of their hair, and cut their throats instead of shaving them. So of course he grew poorer every day, till at last he found himself with nothing left in his house but his wife and his razor, both of whom were as sharp as sharp could be.

For his wife was an exceedingly clever person, who was continually rating her husband for his stupidity; and when she saw they hadn't a farthing left, she fell as usual to scolding.

But the barber took it very calmly. 'What is the use of making such a fuss, my dear?' said he. 'You've told me all this before, and I quite agree with you. I never *did* work, I never *could* work, and I never *will* work. That is the fact!'

'Then you must beg!' returned his wife, 'for *I* will not starve to please you! Go to the palace, and beg something of the King. There is a wedding feast going on, and he is sure to give alms to the poor.'

'Very well, my dear!' said the barber submissively. He was rather afraid of his clever wife, so he did as he was bid, and going to the palace, begged of the King to give him something.

'Something?' asked the King. 'What thing?'

Now the barber's wife had not mentioned anything in particular, and the barber was far too addle-pated to think of anything by himself, so he answered cautiously, 'Oh, something!'

'Will a piece of land do?' said the King.

Whereupon the lazy barber, glad to be helped out of the difficulty, remarked that perhaps a piece of land would do as well as anything else.

Then the King ordered a piece of waste land, outside the city, should be given to the barber, who went home quite satisfied.

'Well! What did you get?' asked the clever wife, who was waiting impatiently for his return. 'Give it me quick, that I may go and buy bread!'

And you may imagine how she scolded when she found he had only got a piece of waste land.

'But land's land!' remonstrated the barber. 'It can't run away, so we must always have something now!'

'Was there ever such a dunderhead?' raged the clever wife. 'What good is ground unless we can till it? And where are we to get bullocks and ploughs?'

But being, as we have said, an exceedingly clever person, she set her wits to work, and soon thought of a plan whereby to make the best of a bad bargain.

She took her husband with her, and set off to the piece of waste land; then, bidding her husband imitate her, she began walking about the field, and peering anxiously into the ground. But when anybody came that way, she would sit down, and pretend to be doing nothing at all.

Now it so happened that seven thieves were hiding in a thicket hard by, and they watched the barber and his wife all day, until they became convinced something mysterious was going on. So at sunset they sent one of their number to try and find out what it was.

'Well, the fact is,' said the barber's wife, after beating about the bush for some time, and with many injunctions to strict secrecy, 'this field belonged to my grandfather, who buried five pots of gold in it, and we were just trying to discover the exact spot before beginning to dig. You won't tell anyone, will you?'

The thief promised he wouldn't, of course, but the mom.
the barber and his wife went home, he called his companior
and telling them of the hidden treasure, set them to work. Ah
night long they dug and delved, till the field looked as if it had
been ploughed seven times over, and they were as tired as tired
could be; but never a gold piece, nor a silver piece, nor a
farthing did they find, so when dawn came they went away
disgusted.

The barber's wife, when she found the field so beautifully
ploughed, laughed heartily at the success of her stratagem,
and going to the corn-dealer's shop, borrowed some rice to sow
in the field. This the corn-dealer willingly gave her, for he
reckoned he would get it back threefold at harvest time. And
so he did, for never was there such a crop!—the barber's wife
paid her debts, kept enough for the house, and sold the rest
for a great crock of gold pieces.

Now when the thieves saw this, they were very angry indeed,
and going to the barber's house, said, 'Give us our share of
the harvest, for we tilled the ground, as you very well know.'

'I told you there was gold in the ground,' laughed the
barber's wife, 'but you didn't find it. I have, and there's a crock
full of it in the house, only you rascals shall never have a farthing of it.'

'Very well!' said the thieves. 'Look out for yourself tonight.
If you won't give us our share we'll take it!'

So that night one of the thieves hid himself in the house,
intending to open the door to his comrades when the housefolk
were asleep; but the barber's wife saw him with the corner of
her eye, and determined to lead him a dance. Therefore, when
her husband, who was in a dreadful state of alarm, asked her
what she had done with the gold pieces, she replied, 'Put them
where no one will find them—under the sweetmeats, in the
crock that stands in the niche by the door.'

The thief chuckled at hearing this, and after waiting till all
was quiet, he crept out, and feeling about for the crock, made

off with it, whispering to his comrades that he had got the prize. Fearing pursuit, they fled to a thicket, where they sat down to divide the spoil.

'She said there were sweetmeats on the top,' said the thief. 'I will divide them first, and then we can eat them, for it is hungry work, this waiting and watching.'

So he divided what he thought were the sweetmeats as well as he could in the dark. Now in reality the crock was full of all sorts of horrible things that the barber's wife had put there on purpose, and so when the thieves crammed its contents into their mouths, you may imagine what faces they made and how they vowed revenge.

But when they returned next day to threaten and repeat their claim to a share of the crop, the barber's wife only laughed at them.

'Have a care!' they cried. 'Twice you have fooled us—once by making us dig all night, and next by feeding us on filth and breaking our caste. It will be our turn tonight!'

Then another thief hid himself in the house, but the barber's wife saw him with half an eye, and when her husband asked, 'What have you done with the gold, my dear? I hope you haven't put it under the pillow?' she answered, 'Don't be alarmed; it is out of the house. I have hung it in branches of the *nim* tree outside. No one will think of looking for it there!'

The hidden thief chuckled, and when the housefolk were asleep he slipped out and told his companions.

'Sure enough, there it is!' cried the captain of the band, peering up into the branches. 'One of you go up and fetch it down.' Now what he saw was really a hornets' nest, full of great big brown and yellow hornets.

So one of the thieves climbed the tree; but when he came close to the nest, and was just reaching up to take hold of it, a hornet flew out and stung him on the thigh. He immediately clapped his hand to the spot.

'Oh, you thief!' cried out the rest from below, 'you're

pocketing the gold pieces, are you? Oh! shabby! shabby!'—
For you see it was very dark, and when the poor man clapped
his hand to the place where he had been stung, they thought
he was putting his hand in his pocket.

'I assure you I'm not doing anything of the kind!' retorted
the thief, 'but there is something that bites in this tree!'

Just at that moment another hornet stung him on the
breast, and he clapped his hand there.

'Fie! fie for shame! We saw you do it that time!' cried the
rest. 'Just you stop that at once, or we will make you!'

So they sent up another thief, but he fared no better, for
by this time the hornets were thoroughly roused, and stung the
poor man all over, so that he kept clapping his hands here,
there, and everywhere.

'Shame! Shabby! Ssh-sh!' bawled the rest; and then one
after another they climbed the tree, determined to share the
booty, and one after another began clapping their hands about
their bodies, till it came to the captain's turn. Then he, intent
on having the prize, seized hold of the hornets' nest, and as
the branch on which they were all standing broke at the
selfsame moment, they all came tumbling down with the
hornets' nest on top of them. And then, in spite of bumps and
bruises, you can imagine what a stampede there was!

After this the barber's wife had some peace, for every one
of the seven thieves was in hospital. In fact, they were laid
up for so long a time that she began to think that they were
never coming back again, and ceased to be on the look-out.

But she was wrong, for one night, when she had left the window open, she was awakened by whisperings outside, and at once recognized the thieves' voices. She gave herself up for lost; but determined not to yield without a struggle, she seized her husband's razor, crept to the side of the window, and stood quite still. By and by the first thief began to creep through cautiously. She just waited till the tip of his nose was visible, and then, flash!—she sliced it off with the razor as clean as a whistle.

'Confound it!' yelled the thief, drawing back mighty quick, 'I've cut my nose on something!'

'Hush-sh-sh-sh!' whispered the others. 'You'll wake someone. Go on!'

'Not I!' said the thief. 'I'm bleeding like a pig!'

'Pooh!—knocked your nose against the shutter, I suppose,' returned the second thief. 'I'll go.'

But, swish!—off went the tip of his nose too.

'Dear me!' said he ruefully, 'there certainly is something sharp inside!'

'A bit of bamboo in the lattice, most likely,' remarked the third thief. 'I'll go!'

And, flick!—off went his nose too.

'It is most extraordinary!' he exclaimed, hurriedly retiring. 'I felt exactly as if someone had cut the tip of my nose off!'

'Rubbish!' said the fourth thief. 'What cowards you all are! Let *me* go!'

But he fared no better, nor the fifth, nor the sixth.

'My friends!' said the captain, when it came to his turn, 'you are all disabled. One man must remain unhurt to protect the wounded. Let us return another night.'—He was a cautious man, you see, and valued his nose.

So they crept away sulkily, and the barber's wife lit a lamp, and gathering up all the nose tips, put them safely in a little box.

Now before the robbers' noses were healed over, the hot weather set in, and the barber and his wife, finding it warm sleeping in the house, put their beds outside; for they made sure the thieves would not return. But they did, and seizing such a good opportunity for revenge, they lifted up the wife's bed, and carried her off fast asleep. She woke to find herself borne along on the heads of four of the thieves, whilst the other three ran beside her. She gave herself up for lost, and though she thought, and thought, and thought, she could find no way of escape; till, as luck would have it, the robbers paused to take breath under a banyan tree. Quick as lightning, she seized hold of a branch that was within reach, and swung herself into the tree, leaving her quilt on the bed just as if she were still in it.

'Let us rest a bit here,' said the thieves who were carrying the bed. 'There is plenty of time, and we are tired. She is dreadfully heavy!'

The barber's wife could hardly help laughing, but she had to keep very still, for it was a bright moonlight night; and the robbers, after setting down their burden, began to squabble as to who should take first watch. At last they determined that it should be the captain, for the others had really barely recovered from the shock of having their noses sliced off; so they lay down to sleep, while the captain walked up and down, watching the bed, and the barber's wife sat perched up in the tree like a great bird.

Suddenly an idea came into her head, and drawing her white veil becomingly over her face, she began to sing softly. The robber captain looked up, and saw the veiled figure of a woman in the tree. Of course he was a little surprised, but being a good-looking young fellow, and rather vain of his appearance, he jumped at once to the conclusion that it was a fairy who had fallen in love with his handsome face. So he twirled his moustaches, and strutted about, waiting for her to speak. But when she went on singing, and took no notice of him, he stopped and called out, 'Come down, my beauty! I won't hurt you!'

But still she went on singing; so he climbed up into the tree, determined to attract her attention. When he came quite close, she turned away her head and sighed.

'What is the matter, my beauty?' he asked tenderly. 'Of course you are a fairy, and have fallen in love with me, but there is nothing to sigh at in that, surely?'

'Ah—ah—ah!' said the barber's wife, with another sigh, 'I believe you're fickle. Men with long-pointed noses always are!'

But the robber captain swore he was the most constant of men; yet still the fairy sighed and sighed, until he almost wished his nose had been shortened too.

'You are telling stories, I am sure!' said the pretended fairy. 'Just let me touch your tongue with the tip of mine, and then I shall be able to taste if there are fibs about!'

So the captain put out his tongue, and snip!—the barber's wife bit the tongue off clean!

What with the fright and the pain, he tumbled off the branch, and fell bump on the ground, where he sat with his legs very wide apart, looking as if he had come from the skies.

'What is the matter?' cried his comrades, awakened by the noise of his fall.

'*Bul-ul-a-bul-ul-ul!*' answered he, pointing up into the tree; for of course he could not speak plainly without the tip of his tongue.

'What—is—the—matter?' they bawled in his ear, as if that would do any good.

'*Bul-ul-a-bul-ul-ul!*' said he, still pointing upwards.

'The man is bewitched!' cried one. 'There must be a ghost in the tree!'

Just then the barber's wife began flapping her veil and howling; whereupon, without waiting to look, the thieves in a terrible fright set off at a run, dragging their leader with them; and the barber's wife, coming down the tree, put her bed on her head, and walked quietly home.

After this, the thieves came to the conclusion that it was no use trying to gain their point by force, so they went to law to claim their share. But the barber's wife pleaded her own cause so well, bringing out the nose and tongue tips as witnesses, that the King made the barber his Wazir, saying, 'He will never do a foolish thing as long as his wife is alive!'

The Cautious Farm Boy

A farmer's son had been told by his mother to be careful when talking to strangers. And the lad had taken the lesson very much to heart.

One day he was minding a herd of pigs in a field when he was hailed from the road by a stranger.

'Whose pigs are those, my boy?' called the traveller by way of opening the conversation.

'That old feller's over there look,' shouted back the farm boy, pointing to the father of the herd.

'Oh, very good indeed!' said the stranger, laughing. 'Now

tell me,' he said, serious again, 'where does this road go to, my boy?'

'Don't go nowhere,' the farm boy answered. ''Tis here every night when I goes home, and 'tis still here next morning when I comes back.'

'Very funny,' said the stranger, not laughing so heartily this time. 'And what's your father's name, laddie?'

'I don't know,' said the boy, eyeing the man ever more suspiciously. 'But if you'll stop here and mind the pigs a bit, I'll go home and ask mother. I dare say she can tell you.'

The Irishman's Hat

Once a while back, an Irishman had fifteen pounds to spare. He didn't want to take it with him where he was going to do a spot of navvying, so he went to a public house and asked the landlord if he would keep five pounds for him.

'Certainly,' said the landlord.

'When I come back,' said the Irishman, 'I don't want everybody knowing my business, so I'll lift my hat and say, "Do you remember the man with the white hat with a green band round it?" Then you give me the money.'

He'd fixed things up in that pub, so off he went to another where he got rid of five more pounds in just the same way; then to a third pub to do it again with the last five pounds.

When his navvying job was finished, the Irishman was given a lift home by a butcher. Of course, after a mile or two they got cracking about money.

The Irishman said, 'I can get money when you can't.'

'Oh aye,' said the butcher, 'and how do you manage that?'

'I'll tell you what,' said the Irishman, 'I'll bet you five pounds I can do it.'

'Done,' said the butcher.

So the Irishman waited till they reached the first of the pubs where he had left money before he said, 'Right. Let's stop here.'

They went inside, the butcher ordered a round of drinks and when the landlord brought them, the Irishman lifted his hat and said, 'Do you remember the man with the white hat with a green band round it?'

'Yes, I do,' said the landlord. 'Here's five pounds for him.'

The butcher just blinked, he was that surprised.

'Come on,' said the Irishman. 'We'll try another pub.'

The same thing happened again. The butcher ordered drinks; the Irishman got his money.

'Once more,' said the Irishman. 'Just once more, to convince you for sure.'

In the third pub everything happened just as twice before.

'By crikey,' said the butcher, 'I think I'll have a go.'

'You'll want this hat then,' said the Irishman. 'But it'll cost you.'

'How much?' asked the butcher.

'Five pounds,' said the Irishman.

'Hand it over,' said the butcher.

The next public house they came to, in they went.

'Two pints please, landlord,' said the butcher.

'Two pints, sir,' said the landlord when he'd drawn them.

The butcher raised his hat.

'Do you remember the man with the white hat with a green band round it?' he said.

'No,' said the landlord, 'I don't. What's the matter with him?'

'Aren't you going to give us five pounds for him?' said the butcher.

'I am not,' said the landlord. 'But I'll tell you what. I'll give you a kick up the backside, if you like.'

'That's five pounds you owe me,' said the Irishman to the butcher.

Letters to the Editor

Trouble with Cockroaches

Sir, Mr Green's interesting article: 'The Trouble with Cockroaches', prompts the following story of an experience of a friend of mine some years ago. Returning late from the club one Saturday night he found everybody in bed, but his kitchen floor alive with cockroaches. Being of a tidy mind he sucked up as many as he could in a vacuum cleaner. Then the

thought that they were not dead but merely snug in the cleaner prompted him to connect it by rubber tubing to a gas tap, and to fill the cleaner with gas. He retired happily to bed and slept late.

Next morning his wife found the cleaner and thought she would clean up a little; she switched on and it promptly blew up! The representative of the manufacturers was called in, and he confessed that he had 'never seen one go up like that before'. My friend kept his silence and eventually got his replacement vacuum cleaner.　　　　R. J. Moreley, Surrey.

Potatogram

Sir, An article in today's issue discusses how to send a message from an express train. Faced with the same problem on the same line, I consulted the steward in charge of the dining car. He provided me with a pencil and paper, made an incision in a large potato, and himself lobbed the potato to the feet of a porter as we ran through Peterborough, with my message wedged in it but clearly visible. The stationmaster did what was necessary. The steward would not take anything; he was glad to be of service.　　　　H. C. V. Mynors, Guildford.

Lazy Jack

There was once a boy called Jack who lived with his mother in a little hut, and who was so lazy that he had never done a day's work in his life. At length his mother got tired of seeing him basking in the sun all day in the summer and lying by the fire in the winter, and she said he should have nothing more to eat or drink from her until he had worked for it. It was root, hog, or die for him from that day on.

So next morning Jack hired himself out to a farmer, and as he was a fine strong fellow he did a good day's work, and the farmer paid him a penny at the end of it. But the great fool lost it on the way home.

So his mother said to him, 'You did ought to have put it in your pocket.'

'I'll do that next time,' said Jack.

Next day Jack hired himself to a cow-keeper, who gave him a jar of milk, and he put it in his pocket and carried it home, and there was hardly a drop left by the time he got back.

So his mother said, 'Why couldn't you carry it on your head?'

'So I will next time,' said Jack.

Next day he went to the farmer again, and got a cream cheese for his pay, and clapped it on his head; but it was a hot day and the cream cheese was soft, and what wasn't stuck in his hair was running down his shoulders by the time he got home.

'You great fool!' said his mother. 'You should have carried it in your hands!'

'Well, then, I will next time,' said Jack.

Next day he went to a miller's who gave him nothing but an old Tom cat for his services, and Jack tried to carry it carefully home in his hands, but he got scratched for his pains, and the cat made off for home.

'Why couldn't you tie it with string and lead it along?' said his mother.

'Don't take on, mother,' said Jack. 'That's what I'll do next time.'

Next day was worst of all, for Jack worked with a butcher, and he did so well that the butcher gave him a fine shoulder of mutton, such as they'd not seen in their house for many a long day. But it didn't look so fine by the time Jack had dragged it back over all the stones and through all the mud on his path home. This time his mother did lose her patience, and she called him all the names she could put her tongue to.

'But what can I do, mother?' asked Jack. 'You tell me different every time.'

'What can you do? Why carry it back on your shoulder,' said his mother, and she thought to herself he couldn't do much harm with that.

The next day Jack went out to work again, this time with a cattle-keeper, who gave him an old donkey at the end of the day. Jack had a great time hoisting it on to his shoulder, but he managed it in the end, and staggered away from the market-place. Now it happened that on his way he passed the house of a rich man who had one only daughter, a very beautiful girl, but she was deaf and dumb and had never laughed in her life, and the doctors had told her father that if she could once be made to laugh she would be cured. Her father had tried all means, but nothing would get even a smile from her, so at last he had said that if any man could make her laugh he should marry her. Well that day she was sitting sadly at her window, and she saw the donkey's legs kicking in the air and Jack sweating away under his burden, and she laughed and laughed, and said, 'Look, father!' And her father was so overjoyed that he ran out and fetched Jack in, and they were married. And Jack fetched his old mother to live with him in a fine house, and they were all happy together.

A Good Trencher

World Champion pie-eater George 'Harpo' Bradley retained his title by eating a $4\frac{1}{2}$ lb pie in 9 min. 30 secs. Then he went home for lunch.

Watched by two hundred cheering spectators, 38-year-old miner George beat three other rivals in a Wallsend-on-Tyne club. He started his day with a hefty ham and egg breakfast in bed. On the way to the championships he stopped at a friend's house for a cup of tea and a snack, 'just to get an appetite up'.

After polishing off the steaming pie, George sank a pint of beer and left for home. He said, 'I told my wife that I wouldn't be late for lunch. She always cooks a good roast on a Sunday—and I'm always ready for it.'

Farmer Gag's Clever Son

Farmer Gag lived at Ruardean in the Forest of Dean and he was behind with his rent. One day, the farmer's youngest son met the landlord, who asked him where his father was.

The lad says, 'He's off making a bad matter worse.'

Landlord says, 'Where's your mother?'

Lad says, 'Baking a batch of bread as was ate last week.'

So the landlord asked where his sister was.

Lad says, 'In the other room crying over the fun she had last Whitsuntide.'

'Well, where's your brother?' asks the landlord.

'Gone hunting,' replies the lad. 'And all the game he kills he leaves behind, and all as he doesn't kill he brings home alive.'

Then the landlord, he says, 'Well, if you come to my house tomorrow at twelve, not before not after, not coming straight down the road, nor across the fields, why, I'll forgive your father the six months' rent he owes.'

The lad, he went the next day, and got there just at twelve o'clock.

'How did you come?' asks the landlord.

'Across the road,' says the lad.

'I told you you were *not* to come down the road nor across the fields.'

'No more I didn't,' says the lad. 'I didn't come *down* the road. I rode the old sheep, and he ran from one hedge to the other across the road all the way, and scratched my face as you can see.'

Then the lad was taken inside for to make his explanations.

'Now,' says the landlord, 'how was your father off making a bad matter worse?'

'The cow died,' replies the lad, 'and father, he was at the pub spending the money as ought to have bought us a new cow.'

'And your mother, who was baking a batch of bread that was eaten last week?'

'So she was. We *hadn't* no bread last week, but borrowed from a neighbour, and when I met you, mother was baking a batch of bread to repay the neighbour with.'

'And your sister, who you said was crying over the fun she had last Whitsuntide, what about her?' asks the landlord.

'She had saved some money, and at Whitsuntide she spent it all. She was crying over that when you met me.'

'And your brother's hunting?' asks the landlord.

'What I said was true,' replies the lad. 'When we met, my brother was under an oak tree hunting fleas, and all he killed he left behind, and all he didn't kill he brought home alive.'

So the landlord, he gave the lad a receipt for the six months' rent that was due.

Horse's Egg

Two cockneys decided to stay a few days in the country. They'd never been out of London before, and being on holiday they were ready for some fun at country folks' expense. They were quite sure, you see, that all countrymen are slow-witted and ignorant.

One morning, as they strolled along a lane, they met an old man who happened to have a fat pumpkin tucked under his arm. The townies saw he was carrying something but they didn't know what it was. Nevertheless, they nudged each other and thought they'd enjoy a joke.

'Good morning, squire,' they said, standing in the old man's path.

'Good marnin', zurs,' said the old man, touching his forelock respectfully.

'And what's that you've got under your arm, then?' asked one of the Londoners.

'That, zur,' said the old man holding out the pumpkin proudly in both hands, 'that, zur, is a horse's egg, zur.'

'A horse's egg!' said the other Londoner.

'You recognize it, zur,' said the countryman. ''Tis clear enough when you zees un close to, bain't it, zur?'

'Well, well,' said the Londoners, not wanting to show their ignorance. 'It's the finest we ever saw.'

'Ah, well, zur,' said the old man, 'there's plenty of common uns about, but this be a thoroughbred un, zur. That's why she looks zo vine.'

The cockneys exchanged glances.

'Will you sell it?' one of them asked.

'Oh, I dunno about that, zur,' said the old man. 'I doan't mind partin' wi' un, but I doan't s'pose you'll pay what I want for zo vine a thoroughbred horse's egg as this, zur.'

'Try us,' said the cockneys.

The bargaining began and went on for some time. In the end a price was agreed, the money exchanged, and the deal concluded with a handshake all round.

'Now mind, zurs,' said the old man, as he parted company with the pumpkin, 'do 'ee take care wi' un, for she'll soon hatch out.'

'We'll be careful,' said the cockneys and went off down the lane, flushed at their unexpected good fortune.

In their haste to get back to their lodgings, they took a short cut that led them up a steep hill. They were almost at the top when the cockney who was carrying the pumpkin tripped and dropped his precious burden.

At once the pumpkin rolled off down the hill, gathering speed as it went, till it ran into a juniper bush growing half way down.

Now it so happened that a hare was hiding under the bush. And as the pumpkin plunged in, the startled hare scampered out.

The two cockneys were chasing after their costly prize. And seeing the pumpkin roll into the bush and the hare come racing out, they thought the pumpkin had hatched. So they ran on after the hare bellowing,

'Hi, stop our colt! Stop our colt!'

The Iron Man

Not many years ago a Harley Street doctor and a number of other experts met in the library of the Society for Psychical Research to investigate the unusual eating habits of a sixty-four-year-old man, Mr Arthur Haylock.

Mr Haylock began his meal by smashing an electric light bulb, sprinkling the pieces with pepper and salt, and eating them like so many bits of broken biscuit.

As he ate, the expert observers questioned Mr Haylock about his performance.

Where had he learned such a skill? they wanted to know. From the fakirs of India, Mr Haylock told them, with whom he had spent twenty years studying the art.

Could he swallow large objects? No, he had to chew everything he ate into little pieces, just as people did with ordinary food. And he demonstrated the point by munching half a dozen razor blades before swallowing them.

To be sure there was no trickery involved, and to check that Mr Haylock was unharmed after tackling such apparently dangerous fare, the doctor shone a torch into the man's mouth.

'All gone except for one small piece,' he reported.

The pepper and salt helped make swallowing easier, Mr Haylock told his investigators, whose curiosity was now so thoroughly aroused that they wanted to know what other unlikely objects he had eaten.

Once a man had brought a fairy-cycle into the garage where Mr Haylock worked and said, 'Eat that.' He cut it up with a hacksaw and made a meal off the bicycle every day. It took him five days to get rid of it all.

He had discovered his ability to eat solid objects when he was a lad of fifteen. He had swallowed a lens from a pair of spectacles. At the hospital, the doctors refused to believe what he had done, so he swallowed the other lens in front of them. Astonished, they X-rayed him and while they did so he ate two pieces of lead and the coins he happened to have in his pocket.

For ten years Mr Haylock toured theatres and fun-fairs eating almost anything offered him by his audiences. Sometimes, he consumed fifteen gramophone records and two hundred razor blades in a day.

Soon he was making over £50 a week—a great deal of money in those days—and at one time was a star performer in Bertram Mills Circus. Doing two shows a day, he lost his appetite for ordinary food, although at other times he ate like anyone else. As a stock for emergencies, Mr Haylock kept a cupboard full of 2,000 worn-out light bulbs and a large pile of old gramophone records.

Not everyone who has tried eating solid objects came off as well as Mr Haylock, however. Mr Goichi Kawakami was found in the streets of Tobata, Japan, doubled up with pain. He was rushed to Kypritsu hospital where doctors diagnosed inflammation of the stomach and operated. Inside, they discovered an extraordinary collection of items:

> 1 piece of wire
> 13 razor blades
> 1 fountain-pen
> 1 toothbrush
> 1 pencil
> 1 pair of chopsticks
> 1 bone from an umbrella
> 21 nails
> *and* 41 other bits of hardware.

Everything had been swallowed during the previous six months.

Later, Mr Kawakami explained that he had been told at a festival that he would win a big prize if he ate such stuff. Unlike Mr Haylock, he had not studied with the Indian fakirs and so did not know the secret of how to digest such a menu!

Work Like a Good 'Un

One day a farmer was walking round his farm, when he heard his man singing in a barn. So he stopped to listen and heard these words:

> 'Bread and cheese, work as you please,
> Bread and cheese, work as you please.'

Then the farmer went and told his wife what he had heard. The farmer's wife said: 'How did he seem to be working?'

'Oh,' he said, 'I peeped through a loop-hole in the barn, and he didn't see me; but I saw him, and he was working as slowly as he could.'

'That'll never do,' she said. 'I'll try him with something better than that.'

So the next day she made a nice plum pudding and an apple pie for the man. Then she told her husband to go and see if he worked any better.

So this time the farmer heard him singing:

> 'Plum pudden and apple pie,
> Do your work accordingly.
> Plum pudden and apple pie,
> Do your work accordingly.'

So the farmer went back to his wife and told her what he had heard.

'How was he working?' she said.

'Much better, but not so fast as he might do,' he replied.

'Oh, well,' she said, 'I'll try him with better food than that.'

So the next day she gave him roast beef and plum pudding, and told her husband to go and see if he worked any better.

So this time the farmer heard him singing:

'Roast beef and plum pudden,
Do your work like a good 'un.
Roast beef and plum pudden,
Do your work like a good 'un.'

Then the farmer told his wife what he had heard, and said the man was working as hard as a horse, and with all his might.

So after this the farmer's wife always fed the man on the best food that she could get, and he worked hard ever after.

84

Parson Spry's Bicycle

When bicycles first came on to the market, they were often called bone-shakers, for they rattled along the rutted roads of those days without the cushioning help of air-filled tyres or saddle springs. Parson Spry, vicar of Sennan and St Levan in Cornwall, decided to buy a bone-shaker for himself. It would be cheaper, he thought, than keeping a horse and would carry him about his parish and from church to church just as well. Except, of course, for going up hills; then he'd have to push his mechanical horse instead of riding it to the top. But he didn't mind that, he said, so long as he could save some money.

As soon as his bicycle arrived, he set off to break it in, and was delighted to discover how fast it ran downhill. He was quite sure that he could beat any horseman. And being a proud sort of chap with a taste for a wager, he stationed himself next market day at the top of Tul-tuf Hill and waited for a suitable contestant to come along. Plenty of horse-riding farmers came by that morning, and each one he challenged to a race. As most of them had never cast eyes on a bicycle before, they put more faith in their mounts than in this newfangled machine and readily took on the parson.

Each time the same thing happened. Off the farmer would go, galloping down Tul-tuf; and gathering speed behind him came Parson Spry and his rattling machine. Soon, he'd be neck and neck and gaining. At which point, the farmer's horse, catching sight of the unfamiliar monster, took fright, bolted, and sent its rider flying over a hedge, or diving nose-down into a ditch, or crashing into the branches of a tree. Meanwhile, on went the speeding parson, victor of the race, to the bottom of the hill, there to crow to all and sundry that his horse was the best in the west.

Until, that is, his last race that Thursday morning. Parson's brimming confidence sent him off too recklessly. His bicycle began to gather too much speed for comfort. And having no brakes to prevent its progress, the machine went on gathering momentum. At last it was quite unmanageable, a runaway whose unfortunate rider could do no more than hang on grimly for dear life.

At the bottom of this hill was Alverton water, which the road crossed not by a bridge but by a ford. There, as the terror-stricken minister plunged towards them, several market-going women sat astride their nags in the middle of the stream, allowing the horses to drink while they enjoyed a gossip and rested their arms from the weight of their baskets, heavy with butter and eggs and cheese. So engrossed were the women in their talk that no one noticed the approaching run-away. And so dumbstruck was the parson by his misadventure that he found himself unable to utter even a cry of warning. So it was that he ploughed like an avenging, bike-borne angel into the midst of this peaceful gathering, his bicycle's spinning wheels spraying water everywhere, before hitting a boulder and tossing him ignominiously into the stream.

Horses, even the best of them, are nervy beasts, disliking sudden appearances. Parson Spry's arrival, unheralded, was not only sudden but violent too. Several horses threw off their mistresses and galloped away; others sidled and pranced, retaining their mounts who, however, in struggling to control their beasts lost hold of their laden baskets, which tumbled into the water and scattered their precious cargoes under the horses' treading hooves.

In less than a minute, the ford was transformed from its former rural pleasance into a noisy mash of tangled, struggling people and animals, all thrashing about among a wreckage of broken baskets and ruined groceries.

Once they had extricated themselves from the fray, and had taken in what had happened, the women grew quite furious and turned their wrath on the cause of their calamity. They took their revenge at first simply by throwing whatever came

to hand at the bedraggled parson. But this only served to whet their appetite for vengeance. So they grabbed the soaked and now bruised victim, and rolled him in the mud, teeming abuse on his head the while. More no doubt would have been done to the wretched man had not some passing farmers intervened to save his skin.

Parson Spry never again trusted his bicycle. And before long, so sociable was he, the offended parishioners forgave him, and life returned to its former ways.

Get Your Hair Cut

A young apprentice was working one day when he thought to himself, 'By heck, it's time I had a hair cut.' So he decided he'd go straightaway to the barber's down the road. He was just setting off when his boss saw him.

'Where d'you think you're going?' asked the boss.

'For a hair cut,' said the apprentice.

'You're what!' said the boss. 'You can't go for a hair cut in my time, laddie.'

'Why not?' asked the apprentice. 'Me hair grew in your time. I don't see why it shouldn't be cut in your time.'

Decoy Ducks

A tenant farmer had an argument with his landlord. For months they argy-bargied, neither one budging an inch for the other. Finally the farmer decided to take the row to court and get it settled there. So he visited his lawyer and talked about how he might win the case. The lawyer didn't hold out much hope. According to him, there was as much right on the landlord's side as on the farmer's.

'Well then,' said the farmer at last, 'how'd it be if I sent the old judge a couple of prime ducks for his dinner?'

'You what!' said the lawyer horrified. 'But that's bribery.'

'Nay,' said the farmer, coy-like. 'T'would be meant as no more than a kindly gift.'

'All I can tell you is this,' replied the lawyer. 'If you want to lose your case, that's the way to do it.'

Well the farmer went to court, and, as much to his lawyer's surprise as to everyone else's, he won.

As he was leaving the courtroom, the farmer turned to his lawyer and said, 'I sent the ducks.'

'You didn't!' said his lawyer.

'I did!' said the farmer. 'But I sent them in landlord's name.'

Mechanical Fault

A woman reported to Southend police that she had seen a car being driven at Leigh-on-Sea with what appeared to be a body protruding from the open boot. Police found the car—with two legs sticking out of the back. They belonged to a garage mechanic trying to trace a noise which was annoying a driver.

A Pottle o' Brains

Once in these parts, and not so long gone neither, there was a fool that wanted to buy a pottle o' brains, for he was ever getting into scrapes through his foolishness, and being laughed at by everyone. Folk told him that he could get everything he liked from the wise woman that lived on the top o' the hill, and dealt in potions and herbs and spells and things, and could tell you all that would come to you or your family. So he told his mother, and asked her if he could seek the wise woman and buy a pottle o' brains.

'That you should,' says she, 'you're in sore need of them, my son. And if I should die, who'd take care of a poor fool such as you, no more fit to look after yourself than an unborn baby? But mind your manners, and speak pretty, my lad, for wise folk are easy mispleased.'

So off he went after his tea, and there she was, sitting by the fire, and stirring a big pot.

'Good ev'ning, missis,' says he, 'it's a fine night.'

'Aye,' says she, and went on stirring.

'It'll maybe rain,' says he, and fidgeted from one foot to t'other.

'Maybe,' says she.

'And 'appen it won't,' says he, and looked out of the window.

''Appen,' says she.

And he scratched his head and twisted his hat in his hands.

'Well,' says he, 'I can't mind nothing else about the weather, but let me see . . . the crops are getting on fine.'

'Fine,' says she.

'And—and—the beasts is fattening,' says he.

'They are,' says she.

'And—and—' says he, and comes to a stop—'I reckon we'll tackle business now, having done the polite talking, like. Have you any brains for to sell?'

'That depends,' says she, 'if you wants king's brains, or soldier's brains, or schoolmaster's brains, I dinna keep them.'

'No, no,' says he, 'just ordinary brains, fit for any fool, same as everyone has about here. Something clean common, like.'

'Aye,' says the wise woman, 'I might manage that, if you'll just help yourself a bit first.'

'How's that, missis?' says he.

'I tell you,' says she. 'Just bring me the heart of the thing you like best of all, and I'll tell you where to get your pottle o' brains.'

'But how can I do that?' says he, scratching his head.

'That's not for me to say,' says she. 'Find out for yourself, my lad, if you don't want to be a fool all your life. But you'll have to read me a riddle so as I can see you've brought the right thing, and if you've got your brains about you. And I've something else to see to now,' says she, 'so good ev'ning to you.' And she carried the pot away into her back room.

So off went the fool to his mother, and told her what the wise woman said.

'I reckon I'll have to kill the pig,' says he, 'for I like fat bacon better than anything.'

'Then do it, lad,' said his mother, 'for certain it'll be a strange and good thing for you, if you can buy a pottle o' brains and be able to look after your own self.'

So he killed the pig, and next day off he went to the wise woman's cottage, and there she sat, reading in a great big book.

'Good ev'ning, missis,' says he, 'I've brought you the heart of the thing I like best of all, and I'll just put it on the table wrapped in a bit of paper.'

'Oh aye?' says she, and looked at him through her spectacles. 'Tell me this then, what runs without feet?'

He scratched his head, and thought and thought, but he couldn't tell.

'Get away,' says she, 'you've not fetched me the right thing yet. I've no brains for you today.' And she clapt the book closed and turned her back.

So off the fool went to tell his mother.

But as he got near the house, out came some folk, running to tell him his mother was dying.

And when he got inside, his mother only looked at him and smiled as if to say she could leave him with a quiet mind since he had got brains enough now to look after himself. And then she died.

So down he sat and the more he thought about it the worse he felt. He minded how she'd nursed him when he was a tiddy brat, and helped him with his lessons, and cooked his dinners, and mended his clothes, and bore with his foolishness. And he felt sorrier and sorrier, till he began to sob and grieve.

'Oh, mother, mother!' says he, 'who'll take care of me now! You shouldn't have left me alone, for I liked you better than everything!'

As he said that, he thought of the words of the wise woman. 'Hi, yi!' says he, 'must I take my mother's heart to her?'

'No! I can't do that,' says he. 'What'll I do! What'll I do to get that pottle o' brains, now I'm alone in the world?'

So he thought and thought and thought, and next day he went and borrowed a sack, and bundled his mother in, and carried it on his shoulder up to the wise woman's cottage.

'Good ev'ning, missis,' says he, 'I reckon I've fetched you the right thing this time, surely,' and he plumped the sack *kerflap!* on the doorstep.

'Maybe,' says the wise woman, 'but read me this, now, what's yellow and shining but isn't gold?'

And he scratched his head, and thought and thought but he couldn't tell.

'You've not hit on the right thing yet, my lad,' says she. 'I doubt but you're a bigger fool than I thought!' And she shut the door in his face.

'Look at that!' says he, and he sat down by the roadside and grieved again.

'I've lost the only two things I cared for, and what else can I find to buy a pottle o' brains with!' and he fair howled, till the tears ran down into his mouth.

Then up came a lass that lived near at hand, and looked at him.

'What's up with you, you fool?' says she.

'Oh, I've killed my pig, and lost my mother and I'm nobbut a fool myself,' says he, sobbing.

'That's bad,' says she, 'and haven't you anybody to look after you?'

'No,' says he, 'and I canna buy my pottle o' brains, for there's nothing I like best left!'

'What are you talking about!' says she.

And down she sits by him, and he told her all about the wise woman and the pig, and his mother, and the riddles, and that he was alone in the world.

'Well,' says she, 'I wouldn't mind looking after you myself.'

'Could you do it?' says he.

'Oh aye,' says she. 'Folks say fools make good husbands, and I reckon I'll have you, if you're willing.'

'Can you cook?' says he.

'Aye, I can,' says she.

'And scrub?'

'Surely.'

'And mend clothes?'

'I can that.'

'I reckon you'll do then as well as anybody,' says he, 'but what'll I do about this wise woman?'

'Oh, wait a bit,' says she, 'something may turn up, and it'll not matter if you're a fool, so long as you've got me to look after you.'

'That's true,' says he, and off they went and got married. She kept his house so clean and neat, and cooked his dinner so fine, that one night he says to her, 'Lass, I'm thinking I like you best of everything after all.'

'That's good,' says she, 'and what then?'

'Have I got to kill you, d'you think, and take your heart up to the wise old woman for that pottle o' brains?'

'Lor, no!' says she, looking scared. 'I winna have that. But see here: you didn't cut out your mother's heart, did you?'

'No; but if I had, maybe I'd have got my pottle o' brains,' says he.

'Not a bit of it,' says she. 'Just you take me, heart and all, and I'll bet I'll help you read the riddles.'

'Can you though?' says he, doubtful like. 'I reckon they're too hard for women.'

'Well,' says she, 'let's see now. Tell me the first.'

'What runs without feet?' says he.

'Why, water!' says she.

'It do,' says he, and scratched his head. 'And what's yellow and shining but isn't gold?'

'Why, the sun!' says she.

'So it be!' says he. 'Come on, we'll go to the wise old woman at once.' And off they went.

As they came up the path, she was sitting at the door, twining straws.

'Good ev'ning, missis,' says he.

'Good ev'ning, fool,' says she.

'I reckon I've fetched you the right thing at last,' says he.

The wise woman looked at them both, and wiped her spectacles.

'Can you tell me what that is as has first no legs, and then two legs, and ends with four legs?'

And the fool scratched his head, and thought and thought, but he couldn't tell.

And the lass whispered in his ear, 'It's a tadpole.'

'Happen,' says he then, 'it may be a tadpole, missis.'

The wise woman nodded her head. 'That's right,' says she,

'and you've got a pottle o' brains already.'

'Where be they?' says he, looking about and feeling in his pockets.

'In your wife's head,' says she. 'The only cure for a fool is a good wife to look after him, and that you've got, so good ev'ning to you!' And with that she nodded to them, and up and into the house.

So they went home together, and he never wanted to buy a pottle o' brains again, for his wife had enough for both.

The Mean Farmer's Apples

There was a mean old farmer whose orchard bore the best apples for miles around. Naturally, the local lads, and some jaunty men too, made forays to thieve the fruit.

One year the farmer thought of a way to foil these attacks on his property. He put up a large notice which said:

PLEASE DO NOT TOUCH THE APPLES
THEY ARE WANTED FOR HARVEST FESTIVAL

For a day or two, all was well. Then one morning the farmer went to check the orchard and found the just-ripening apples gone, every one. And there was his notice, turned back to front, and a message scrawled:

ALL IS SAFELY GATHERED IN

Master of All Masters

A girl went to a fair to hire herself as a servant. At last a funny-looking old gentleman engaged her, and took her home to his house. When she got there, he told her that he had something to teach her, for in his house he had his own names for things.

He said to her, 'What will you call me?'

'Master or mister, or whatever you please, sir,' said the girl.

He said, 'You must call me "master of all masters". And what would you call this?' he asked her then, pointing to his bed.

'Bed or couch, or whatever you please, sir.'

'No,' said the old man. 'That's my "barnacle".' He pointed to his trousers. 'And what do you call these?'

'Breeches or trousers,' said the girl, 'or whatever you please.'

'You must call them "squibs and crackers".' Now he pointed to the cat. 'And what would you call her?' he asked.

'Cat or kit, or whatever, sir.'

'You must call her "white-faced simminy". And this?' he asked, showing her the fire. 'What would you call this?'

'Fire or flame, maybe?'

'You must call it "hot cockalorum". And what this?' he went on, pointing to the water.

'Water or wet, or what you like, sir.'

'No. "Pondalorum" is its name. And what would you call all this?' he asked as he pointed to the whole house.

'House or cottage, sir?'

'You must call it "high topper mountain".'

That night the servant woke up her master in a great fright and shouted, 'Master of all masters, get out of your barnacle and put on your squibs and crackers. For white-faced simminy has got a spark of hot cockalorum on its tail, and unless you get some pondalorum, high topper mountain will be all on hot cockalorum.'

The Devil and the Tailor

There was a tailor in our town,
Who was a worthy wight;
    All through the day
    He worked away,
And halfway through the night.

He had a wife whom he did love,
And he had children bright;
    To find the meat
    For them to eat,
Did puzzle the tailor quite.

One day as on the board he sat,
When cupboard and shelf were bare,
    The children cried,
    Unsatisfied
With feeding on the air.

Oh! then unto himself he said,
'Ah! would that I were rich,
    With meat galore,
    And money in store,
And never a coat to stitch.

'If Old Nick now to me would say,
"In riches you may roll,"
   I'm sure I'd sell
   To the Lord of Hell
Myself, both body and soul.'

The Devil unto the tailor came,
And thus to him said he,
   'This bag of gold
   Is wealth untold,
And emptied ne'er shall be.

'Exhaustless is its boundless store,
And it shall all be thine
   Whilst thou hast breath,
   But at thy death
Thy soul shall then be mine.'

'Nay, put the matter as a bet,
Thy bag against my soul;
   We each will take
   A coat to make,
The quickest to take the whole.'

Old Nick to this at once agreed,
And thought the tailor to wheedle;
   'My sight is bad,
   So I'll be glad,
If you will thread my needle.'

'A needleful I'll put you in,'
The tailor said, 'with pleasure,
   Sound and true,
   To last all through
The job we are to measure.'

A needleful he put him in,
The tailor did, with pleasure,
Sound and true,
To last all through
A hundred yards by measure.

To work the two did settle then:
The tailor worked in dread;
The Devil flew
The room all through,
With his hundred yards of thread.

But though the Devil beat his wings,
And panted fit to burst,
With shorter thread,
And clearer head,
The tailor finished first.

Thus was the Devil overcome,
And fairly left i' the lurch;
The tailor wight
Became a knight,
And always went to church.

He patronized charities,
And never joined a revel;
To end my song,
I think it wrong
To swindle—e'en the Devil.

No Clock

A farmer was driving sheep across the hills from Bolton-by-Bowland in Lancashire when he was hailed by a woman who came out of her cottage on the far side of the moor and shouted, 'What time is it?'

The farmer yelled back, 'Three o'clock,' and added, 'have you no clock up theer?'

'No,' came the reply.

'How do you manage then?' asked the farmer.

'We eat when we're hungry,' called back the woman,
'We sup when we're dry,
 Go to bed when we're weary
 And get up when we can't lie.'

Hereafterthis

Once upon a time there was a farmer called Jan, and he lived all alone by himself in a little farmhouse.

By and by he thought he would like to have a wife to keep it all vitty for him.

So he went a-courting a fine maid, and said to her, 'Will you marry me?'

'That I will, to be sure,' said she.

So they went to church and were wed. After the wedding was over, she got up on his horse behind him, and he brought her home. And they lived as happy as the day was long.

One day, Jan said to his wife, 'Wife, can you milk-y?'

'Oh, yes, Jan, I can milk-y. Mother used to milk-y, when I lived home.'

So he went to market, and bought her ten red cows. All went well till one day when she had driven them to the pond to drink, she thought they did not drink fast enough. So she drove them right into the pond to make them drink faster, and they were all drowned.

When Jan came home, she up and told him what she had done, and he said, 'Oh, well there, never mind, my dear; better luck next time.'

So they went on for a bit, and then one day, Jan said to his wife, 'Wife, can you serve pigs?'

'Oh, yes, Jan, I can serve pigs. Mother used to serve pigs when I lived home.'

So Jan went to market and bought her some pigs. All went well till one day, when she had put their food into the trough she thought they did not eat fast enough, and she pushed their heads into the trough to make them eat faster, and they were all choked.

When Jan came home, she up and told him what she had done, and he said, 'Oh, well, there, never mind, my dear; better luck next time.'

So they went on for a bit, and then, one day, Jan said to his wife, 'Wife, can you bake-y?'

'Oh, yes, Jan, I can bake-y. Mother used to bake-y when I lived home.'

So he bought everything for his wife, so that she could bake bread. All went well for a bit, till one day she thought she would bake white bread for a treat for Jan. So she carried her meal to the top of a high hill, and let the wind blow on it, for she thought to herself that the wind would blow out all the bran. But the wind blew away meal, bran, and all—so there was an end of it.

When Jan came home, she up and told him what she had done, and he said, 'Oh, well, there, never mind, my dear; better luck next time.'

So they went on for a bit, and then, one day, Jan said to his wife, 'Wife, can you brew-y?'

'Oh, yes, Jan, I can brew-y. Mother used to brew-y, when I lived home.'

So he bought everything proper for his wife to brew ale with. All went well for a bit, till one day when she had brewed her ale and had put it in the barrel, a big black dog came in and looked up in her face. She drove him out of the house, but he stayed outside the door and still looked up in her face. And she got so angry that she pulled out the plug of the barrel, threw it at the dog, and said, 'What dost look in me for? I be Jan's wife.' Then the dog ran down the road, and she ran after him to chase him right away. When she came back again, she found that the ale had all run out of the barrel, and so there was an end of it.

When Jan came home, she up and told him what she had done, and he said, 'Oh well, there, never mind, my dear; better luck next time.'

So they went on for a bit, and then one day she thought to herself, ''Tis time to clean up my house.' When she was taking down her big bed she found a bag of money on the tester. So when Jan came home, she up and said to him, 'Jan, what is that bag of money on the tester for?'

'That is for Hereafterthis, my dear.'

Now, there was a robber outside the window, and he heard what Jan said. Next day, he waited till Jan had gone to market, and then he knocked at the door.

'What do you please to want?' said Jan's wife.

'I am Hereafterthis,' said the robber. 'I have come for the bag of money.'

Now the robber was dressed like a fine gentleman, so she thought to herself it was very kind of so fine a man to come for the bag of money, so she ran upstairs and fetched the bag of money, and gave it to the robber and he went away with it.

When Jan came home, she said to him, 'Jan, Hereafterthis has been for the bag of money.'

'What do you mean, wife?' said Jan.

So she up and told him, and he said, 'Then I'm a ruined man, for that money was to pay our rent with. The only thing we can do is to roam the world.'

Then Jan took the house door off its hinges. 'That's all we shall have to lie on,' he said. So Jan put the door on his back, and they both set out to look for Hereafterthis. Many a long day they went, and in the night Jan used to put the door on the branches of a tree, and they would sleep on it. One night they came to a big hill, and there was a high tree at the foot. So Jan put the door up in it, and they got up in the tree and went to sleep.

By and by Jan's wife heard a noise, and she looked to see what it was. It was an opening of a door in the side of the hill. Out came two gentlemen with a long table, and behind them fine ladies and gentlemen, each carrying a bag, and one of them was Hereafterthis with the bag of money. They sat round the table, and began to eat and drink and talk and count up all the money in the bags. So then Jan's wife woke him up, and asked what they should do.

'Now's our time,' said Jan, and he pushed the door off the branches, and it fell right in the very middle of the table, and frightened the robbers so that they all ran away. Then Jan and his wife got down from the tree, took as many money-bags as they could carry on the door, and went straight home. And Jan bought his wife more cows, and more pigs, and they lived happily ever after.

Messingham Bells

A time ago a stranger was passing through Messingham in Lincolnshire when he came upon three men sitting on a stile by the churchyard.

'Come to church, Thompson,' one of the three bellowed as the stranger approached.

'Come to church, Brown,' shouted the second man as the stranger reached him.

'Come to church, Carter,' yelled the third man.

The stranger stopped in his tracks.

'Why are you shouting like that?' he asked.

'Ah, well now, you see, sir,' said the first man, 'the church don't have no bells to ring.'

'So we call folks to the services by shouting their names, sir,' said the second man.

'What a pity it is,' said the stranger, 'that your church has no bells.'

'That it is,' said the third man.

'Well now, look here,' said the stranger. 'I'm wealthy enough. If I was to pay for them, could you fellows see that three bells were made for your church?'

'For sure, sir,' said the first man.

'That we could, sir,' said the second.

'Indeed,' said the third, 'just leave it to us, sir.'

So the bargain was struck and the stranger went happily on his way.

When he visited the village again, the bells were finished and hung. But he was astonished to hear the noise they made.

Ting, Tong, Pluff, they went. *Ting, Tong, Pluff*.

'Whatever's the matter?' said the stranger to the three men. 'Why do the bells make such an odd noise. You made them, didn't you?'

'That we did, sir,' said the first man. 'The one I made, 'tis my best handiwork.'

'I used the best materials in mine, sir,' said the second. 'We all did.'

'Aye,' said the third. 'You'll not get better workmanship anywhere.'

'Then why do the bells make those noises? Ting, Tong, Pluff! That's hardly what you expect from good, sound bells.'

He paused for a moment.

'You men are bell-founders, aren't you?' he said.

'Why bless you, sir,' said the first man. 'No. No. Not at all. I'm a tinker by trade.'

'And me, I'm a carpenter, sir.'

'A shoemaker, that's me, sir,' said the third.

So it was that the Messingham bells came to be made of tin, wood and leather. And that's why they rang with such unlikely voices. *Ting, Tong, Pluff*.

You Do My Job, I'll Do Yours

Once on a time there was a man, so surly and cross, he never thought his wife did anything right in the house. So, one evening, in hay-making time, he came home, scolding and swearing, and showing his teeth and making dust.

'Dear love, don't be so angry; there's a good man,' said his goody. 'Tomorrow let's change our work. I'll go out with the mowers and mow, and you shall mind the house at home.'

Yes! the husband thought that would do very well. He was quite willing, he said.

So, early next morning, his goody took a scythe over her neck, and went out into the hay-field with the mowers, and began to mow; but the man was to mind the house, and do the work at home.

First of all, he wanted to churn the butter; but when he had churned a while, he got thirsty, and went down to the cellar to tap a barrel of ale. So, just when he had knocked in the bung, and was putting the tap into the cask, he overheard the pig come into the kitchen. Then off he ran up the cellar steps, with the tap in his hand, as fast as he could, to look after the pig, lest it should upset the churn; but when he got up, and saw the pig had already knocked the churn over, and stood there, routing and grunting amongst the cream which was running all over the floor, he got so wild with rage that he quite forgot the ale-barrel, and ran at the pig as hard as he could. He caught it, too, just as it ran out of doors, and gave it such a kick, that piggy lay for dead on the spot. Then all at once he remembered he had the tap in his hand; but when he got down to the cellar, every drop of ale had run out of the cask.

Then he went into the dairy and found enough cream left to

fill the churn again, and so he began to churn, for butter they must have at dinner. When he had churned a bit, he remembered that their milking cow was still shut up in the byre, and hadn't had a bit to eat or a drop to drink all the morning, though the sun was high. Then all at once he thought 'twas too far to take her down to the meadow, so he'd just get her up on the house top—for the house, you must know, was thatched with sods, and a fine crop of grass was growing there. Now their house lay close up against a steep down, and he thought if he laid a plank across to the thatch at the back he'd easily get the cow up.

But still he couldn't leave the churn, for there was his little babe crawling about on the floor, and 'if I leave it,' he thought, 'the child is safe to upset it.' So he took the churn on his back, and went out with it; but then he thought he'd better first water the cow before he turned her out on the thatch; so he took up a bucket to draw water out of the well; but, as he stooped down at the well's brink, all the cream ran out of the churn over his shoulders, and so down into the well.

Now it was near dinner-time, and he hadn't even got the butter yet; so he thought he'd best boil the porridge, and he filled the pot with water, and hung it over the fire. When he had done that, he thought the cow might perhaps fall off the thatch and break her legs or her neck. So he got up on the house to tie her up. One end of the rope he made fast to the cow's neck, and the other he slipped down the chimney and tied round his own thigh; and he had to make haste, for the water now began to boil in the pot, and he had still to grind the oatmeal.

So he began to grind away; but while he was hard at it, down fell the cow off the house-top after all, and as she fell, she dragged the man up the chimney by the rope. There he stuck fast; and as for the cow, she hung half way down the wall, swinging between heaven and earth, for she could neither get down nor up.

And now the goody had waited seven lengths and seven breadths for her husband to come and call them home to dinner; but never a call they had. At last she thought she'd waited long enough, and went home. But when she got there and saw the cow hanging in such an ugly place, she ran up and cut the rope in two with her scythe. But as she did this, down came her husband out of the chimney; and so when his old dame came inside the kitchen, there she found him standing on his head in the porridge pot.

Who's Crazy Now?

A man called Ricks kept an inn near Acorn Bridge not far from Stratton St Margaret in Wiltshire. He had a son he could do nothing with. The lad was either headstrong or mad, and his father chose to think him mad. That way, you see, old Ricks could get shut of his son into the workhouse, as people did in those days with folk that were sick in the head.

In the end, that's what happened. Young Ricks was carted off to the workhouse at Stratton. But the lad couldn't have been as daft as his father made out, nor stupid neither, because he was as hard to handle in the workhouse as he ever had been at home. From the minute he got there he refused to do anything at all. He wouldn't even eat.

The workhouse master, hoping to break young Ricks's stubborn wilfulness, had him locked in the dead-house all night. He was sure the lad would be frightened being in that cold vault with dead bodies all around. But Ricks wasn't. Not a bit. The corpses terrified him not at all.

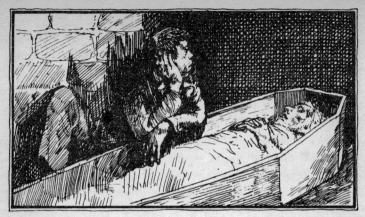

During the night he got so bored he started looking into the coffins just out of curiosity, to see what the dead bodies were like. And it was then he had an idea for getting his own back on the workhouse master for locking him down there.

He opened one of the coffins and lifted out the corpse. Then he took off his own clothes and dressed the corpse in them; and he dressed himself in the dead man's shroud. When he had done this, he stood the body against the wall, just inside the door, before lying down himself in the coffin.

Early in the morning, the workhouse master brought food for his prisoner. Unlocking the door, he approached the corpse standing against the wall, held out the food, and said:

'Will you have it now?'

No answer.

'Will you have it now, lad?' he asked again. 'Or am I to leave you down here all today?'

At that moment young Ricks jumped up in his coffin and called out:

'If he won't have it, I will!'

The workhouse master took one look at the shroud-clad figure standing in the coffin, dropped the food and ran off. Poor fellow, the shock was so great he died soon after. But young Ricks, he had to stay in the workhouse for the rest of his life.

Buyer and Seller

A greengrocer hired a Chinaman to sell oranges at Paddington Station. As it happened, the Chinaman knew no English so the greengrocer taught him how to answer the most probable questions that customers might ask.

The first question was, How much are the oranges? The answer to which would be, Ten pence.

The second question was, Are they juicy? And the reply, Some are, some aren't.

Should the customer then say he would not buy, the Chinaman was to say, If you don't someone else will.

Having learned his replies parrot-fashion, the Chinaman went off to the station and set up his stall.

Before long a passenger rushed up.

'What time is the next train to Cheltenham?' he asked.

'Ten pence,' said the Chinaman.

Annoyed at what he thought was a joke against him, the passenger said, 'Is everyone in the place as daft as you?'

'Some are, some aren't,' said the Chinaman.

'Look here,' said the passenger, losing his temper completely now, 'if you try to make a fool out of me, I'll hit you over the head with my umbrella.'

Innocently, the Chinaman replied, 'If you don't someone else will.'

Carriage Paid

A newspaper of 8 January 1821 reports that Mr Huddy, the ninety-seven-year-old postmaster of Lismore, made a bet. He claimed he could travel from Lismore to Fermoy in a Dungarvon oyster-tub drawn by a pig, a badger, two cats, a goose, and a hedgehog, and that he could do so wearing a large red nightcap on his head, and carrying a pig-driver's whip in one hand and a cow's horn in the other on which he would blow to encourage his team and announce to everyone on his route that he was coming. It was no idle boast. Mr Huddy did it, and won his bet.

Notice to All Employees

Some time between starting and quitting time, without infringing on lunch periods, coffee breaks, rest periods, story-telling, holiday planning, and the re-hashing of yesterday's TV programmes, we ask that each employee try to find some time for a work break. *Signed:* The Manager.

Hudden and Dudden and Donald O'Neary

There was once upon a time two farmers, and their names were Hudden and Dudden. They had poultry in their yards, sheep on the uplands, and scores of cattle in the meadow-land alongside the river. But for all that they weren't happy. For just between their two farms there lived a poor man by the name of Donald O'Neary. He had a hovel over his head and a strip of grass that was barely enough to keep his one cow, Daisy, from starving, and, though she did her best, it was but seldom that Donald got a drink of milk or a roll of butter from Daisy. You would think there was little here to make Hudden and Dudden jealous, but so it is, the more one has the more one wants, and Donald's neighbours lay awake at night scheming how they might get hold of his little strip of grass-land. Daisy, poor thing, they never thought of; she was just a bag of bones.

One day Hudden met Dudden, and they were soon grumbling as usual, and all to the tune of 'If only we could get that vagabond Donald O'Neary out of the country.'

'Let's kill Daisy,' said Hudden at last; 'if that doesn't make him clear out, nothing will.'

No sooner said than agreed, and it wasn't dark before Hudden and Dudden crept up to the little shed where lay poor Daisy trying her best to chew the cud, though she hadn't had as much grass in the day as would cover your hand. And when Donald came to see if Daisy was all snug for the night, the poor beast had only time to lick his hand once before she died.

Well, Donald was a shrewd fellow, and downhearted though he was, begun to think if he could get any good out of Daisy's death. He thought and he thought, and the next day you could have seen him trudging off early to the fair, Daisy's hide over his shoulder, every penny he had jingling in his pockets. Just before he got to the fair, he made several slits in the hide, put a penny in each slit, walked into the best inn of the town as bold as if it belonged to him, and, hanging the hide up on a nail in the wall, sat down.

'Some of your best whisky,' says he to the landlord. But the landlord didn't like his looks. 'Is it fearing I won't pay you, you are?' says Donald. 'Why I have a hide here that gives me all the money I want.' And with that he hit it a whack with his stick and out hopped a penny. The landlord opened his eyes, as you may fancy.

'What'll you take for that hide?'

'It's not for sale, my good man.'

'Will you take a gold piece?'

'It's not for sale, I tell you. Hasn't it kept me and mine for years?' and with that Donald hit the hide another whack and out jumped a second penny.

Well, the long and the short of it was that Donald let the hide go, and, that very evening, who but he should walk up to Hudden's door?

'Good evening, Hudden. Will you lend me your best pair of scales?'

Hudden stared and Hudden scratched his head, but he lent the scales.

When Donald was safe at home, he pulled out his pocketful of bright gold and began to weigh each piece in the scales. But Hudden had put a lump of butter at the bottom, and so the last piece of gold stuck fast to the scales when he took them back to Hudden.

If Hudden had stared before, he stared ten times more now, and no sooner was Donald's back turned, than he was off as hard as he could pelt to Dudden's.

'Good evening, Dudden. That vagabond, bad luck to him—'

'You mean Donald O'Neary?'

'And who else would I mean? He's back here weighing out sackfuls of gold.'

'How do you know that?'

'Here are my scales that he borrowed, and here's a gold piece sticking to them.'

Off they went together, and they came to Donald's door. Donald had finished making the last pile of ten gold pieces. And he couldn't finish because a piece had stuck to the scales.

In they walked without an 'If you please' or 'By your leave'.

'Well *I* never!' That was all *they* could say.

'Good evening, Hudden; good evening, Dudden. Ah! you thought you had played me a fine trick, but you never did me a better turn in all your lives. When I found poor Daisy dead, I thought to myself, "Well, her hide may fetch me something"; and it did. Hides are worth their weight in gold in the market just now.'

Hudden nudged Dudden, and Dudden winked at Hudden.

'Good evening, Donald O'Neary.'

'Good evening, kind friends.'

The next day there wasn't a cow or calf that belonged to Hudden or Dudden but their hide was going to the fair in

Hudden's biggest cart drawn by Dudden's strongest pair of horses.

When they came to the fair, each one took a hide over his arm, and there they were walking through the fair, bawling out at the top of their voices: 'Hides to sell! hides to sell!'

Out came the tanner:

'How much for your hides, my good men?'

'Their weight in gold.'

'It's early in the day to come out of the tavern.' That was all the tanner said, and back he went to his yard.

'Hides to sell! Fine fresh hides to sell!'

Out came the cobbler.

'How much for your hides, my men?'

'Their weight in gold.'

'Is it making game of me you are! Take that for your pains,' and the cobbler dealt Hudden a blow that made him stagger.

Up the people came running from one end of the fair to the other. 'What's the matter? What's the matter?' cried they.

'Here are a couple of vagabonds selling hides at their weight in gold,' said the cobbler.

'Hold 'em fast; hold 'em fast!' bawled the innkeeper, who was the last to come up, he was so fat. 'I'll wager it's one of the rogues who tricked me out of thirty gold pieces yesterday for a wretched hide.'

It was more kicks than halfpence that Hudden and Dudden got before they were well on their way home again, and they didn't run the slower because all the dogs of the town were at their heels.

Well, as you may fancy, if they loved Donald little before, they loved him less now.

'What's the matter, friends?' said he, as he saw them tearing along, their hats knocked in, and their coats torn off, and their faces black and blue. 'Is it fighting you've been? Or mayhap you met the police, ill luck to them?'

'We'll police you, you vagabond. It's mighty smart you

thought yourself, deluding us with your lying tales.'

'Who deluded you? Didn't you see the gold with your own two eyes?'

But it was no use talking. Pay for it he must, and should. There was a meal-sack handy, and into it Hudden and Dudden popped Donald O'Neary, tied him up tight, ran a pole through the knot, and off they started for the Brown Lake of the Bog, each with a pole-end on his shoulder, and Donald O'Neary between.

But the Brown Lake was far, the road was dusty, Hudden and Dudden were sore and weary, and parched with thirst. There was an inn by the roadside.

'Let's go in,' said Hudden, 'I'm dead beat. It's heavy he is for the little he had to eat.'

If Hudden was willing, so was Dudden. As for Donald, you may be sure he wasn't asked, but he was lumped down at the inn door for all the world as if he had been a sack of potatoes.

'Sit still, you vagabond,' said Dudden, 'if we don't mind waiting, you needn't.'

Donald held his peace, but after a while he heard the glasses clink, and Hudden singing away at the top of his voice.

'I won't have her, I tell you; I won't have her!' said Donald. But nobody heeded what he said.

'I won't have her, I tell you; I won't have her!' said Donald, and this time he said it louder; but nobody heeded what he said.

'I won't have her, I tell you; I won't have her!' said Donald; and this time he said it as loud as he could.

'And who won't you have, may I be so bold as to ask?' said a farmer, who had just come up with a drove of cattle, and was turning in for a glass.

'It's the king's daughter. They are bothering the life out of me to marry her.'

'You're the lucky fellow. I'd give something to be in your shoes.'

'Do you see that now! Wouldn't it be a fine thing for a farmer to be marrying a princess, all dressed in gold and jewels?'

'Jewels, do you say? Ah, now, couldn't you take me with you?'

'Well, you're an honest fellow, and as I don't care for the king's daughter, though she's as beautiful as the day and is covered with jewels from top to toe, you shall have her. Just undo the cord, and let me out; they tied me up tight, as they knew I'd run away from her.'

Out crawled Donald; in crept the farmer.

'Now lie still, and don't mind the shaking; it's only rumbling over the palace steps you'll be. And maybe they'll abuse you for a vagabond, who won't have the king's daughter; but you needn't mind that. Ah! it's a deal I'm giving up for you, sure as it is that I don't care for the princess.'

'Take my cattle in exchange,' said the farmer; and you may guess it wasn't long before Donald was at their tails driving them homewards.

Out came Hudden and Dudden, and the one took one end of the pole, and the other the other.

'I'm thinking he's heavier,' said Hudden.

'Ah, never mind,' said Dudden, 'it's only a step now to the Brown Lake.'

'I'll have her now! I'll have her now!' bawled the farmer, from inside the sack.

'By my faith, and you shall though,' said Hudden, and he laid his stick across the sack.

'I'll have her! I'll have her!' bawled the farmer, louder than ever.

'Well, here you are,' said Dudden, for they were now come to the Brown Lake, and, unslinging the sack, they pitched it plumb into the lake.

'You'll not be playing your tricks on us any longer,' said Hudden.

'True for you,' said Dudden. 'Ah, Donald, my boy, it was an ill day when you borrowed my scales.'

Off they went, with a light step and an easy heart, but when they came near home, who should they see but Donald O'Neary, and all around him the cows were grazing, and the calves were kicking up their heels and butting their heads together.

'Is it you, Donald?' said Dudden. 'Faith, you've been quicker than we have.'

'True for you, Dudden, and let me thank you kindly; the turn was good, if the will was ill. You'll have heard, like me, that the Brown Lake leads to the Land of Promise. I always put it down as lies, but it is just as true as my word. Look at the cattle.'

Hudden stared, and Dudden gaped; but they couldn't get over the cattle; fine fat cattle they were too.

'It's only the worst I could bring up with me,' said Donald O'Neary. 'The others were so fat, there was no driving them. Faith, too, it's little wonder they didn't care to leave, with grass as far as you could see, and as sweet and juicy as fresh butter.'

'Ah, now, Donald, we haven't always been friends,' said Dudden, 'but, as I was just saying, you were ever a decent lad, and you'll show us the way, won't you?'

'I don't see that I'm called upon to do that; there is a power more cattle down there. Why shouldn't I have them all to myself?'

'Faith, they may well say, the richer you get, the harder the heart. You always were a neighbourly lad, Donald. You wouldn't wish to keep the luck all to yourself?'

'True for you, Hudden, though 'tis a bad example you set for me. But I'll not be thinking of old times. There is plenty for all three, so come along with me.'

Off they trudged, with a light heart and an easy step. When they came to the Brown Lake, the sky was full of little white

clouds, and, if the sky was full, the lake was as full.

'Ah! now, look, there they are,' cried Donald, as he pointed to the clouds in the lake.

'Where? where?' cried Hudden, and 'Don't be greedy!' cried Dudden, as he jumped his hardest to be first up with the fat cattle. But if he jumped first, Hudden wasn't long behind.

They never came back. Maybe they got too fat, like the cattle. As for Donald O'Neary, he had cattle and sheep all his days to his heart's content.

Silly Jack and the Landlord

There was this old woman, you see, who had a little wee cottage place. And she had one son and she called him Jack. He was a bit off his head, was Jack, a bit short up top like. But she worshipped him all the same. He was the only company she had and of course he did all the work about the place and he was no bother and she was his mother and he was her only bairn, so she thought the world of him. They were poor, awful poor; it was all they could do to keep themselves.

Anyway, one day the old woman was going away from home for a bit and she said before she went,

'Now, Jack,' she says, 'I'm going away from home the day, but I'll maybe be back in time before the landlord goes. He'll be here, like as not, this afternoon sometime. Make sure you have a good fire going so he'll be nice and warm while he's waiting for me.'

'Right, ma,' says Jack. 'I'll have a good fire on,' he says, 'and I'll have it going lovely for when the landlord comes.'

'Good lad,' says his mother, 'that's what to do and I'll not be gone long.'

And away the old woman went.

She'd been away an hour or two when the landlord drops in, wanting his rent, you see. And he says,

'Is your mother in, Jack?'

'No, no,' says Jack, 'me mother's away the day. But she telt me to tell you to sit down and get yourself nice and warm and she'll not be long before she's back. Then she'll give you the money.'

'Right-o,' says the landlord. 'I'll just park my body here by your lovely fire, Jack, and rest my legs like.'

So he sat down in a chair right in front of Jack's great big fire. It was a cold day and the landlord was glad enough to make himself as comfortable as he could. And before long he was fast asleep from the heat of the fire.

Poor Jack, he was sitting at the other side of the fire trying to make himself as comfortable as he could till his mother came in. And while he sat there he kept his eyes on the landlord all the time.

So there they sat, Jack wide awake, watching the landlord fast asleep.

All of a sudden a great big nasty bluebottle settled itself on the landlord's brow and started walking up and down all over the landlord's baldy head. Jack watched it, fascinated. After a bit, him being simple you know, he got himself all worked up about this fly.

'Get off the landlord's head, man!' he says to the fly.

Of course, the fly didn't budge.

Jack waits a bit. Fly walks round the baldy head some more. So Jack has another go.

'Get off the landlord's head, man!' he says.

But fly still takes no notice and poor Jackie gets himself into a right lather.

'Get off the landlord's head, I tell you!' he says.

Fly stays put.

'You're not going to get off, are you?' Jack says. And now he's lost his temper altogether. So he picks up the axe he used to chop sticks for the fire, and he fetches the fly such a hefty wallop that he kills it right enough. But, of course, at the same time he chops a hole in the landlord's baldy head and kills the poor chap stone dead as well.

When Jack's mother got home she found the landlord lying on the floor with his head hammered in two with the axe. She knows straightaway it had been done by her poor daft son, and this time it was something he wouldn't get away with. She'd lose him and he'd be put in prison for the rest of his life. And naturally, him being all she had, she was going to put up a fight to save him somehow. So she sat herself down to think.

Now Jackie wasn't very bright, but he wasn't as daft as his mother made him out to be neither. And she decided the only way to save him was to make him look a lot sillier than he really was. He had to seem a right idiot.

As it happened, Jack and his mother kept a big billy-goat, and they called it 'The Landlord', as a joke, you see. The goat was always chasing folk to butt them, and the landlord was always chasing them to dun for his rent. And this gave the old woman an idea.

First of all she made poor Jackie help her dig a grave in the back garden of the cottage. Then he had to help her carry the landlord's body out and bury it there. The old woman knew Jack would let on to the police where the landlord was when they came nosing about asking questions. So next thing she did was send Jack out for some odds and ends in town. And while he was gone, she dug a second grave a bit off in the woods. After that, she dug up the landlord, dragged his body to the grave in the wood and buried him there.

With him safely out of the way, she went back home, got the big billy-goat into the grave in the back garden, killed him there and buried him.

She had her work cut out to do all that on her own before Jack got back, but she managed somehow. She was a tough old soul, I'll give her that!

But she wasn't done yet, not by a long chalk. When Jackie came back from town, his mother was waiting for him.

'There's sommat wrong with the chimney,' she says. 'I'm going up on the roof to see if there's anything up there. I want you to look up the chimney when I tell you.'

'Right, ma,' Jack says and sets himself in the hearth waiting to poke his head up the flue.

His mother went out the back and climbed up a ladder on to the roof. She took with her a big pan of cold porridge left over from that morning's breakfast. When she was beside the chimney, she yells down,

'All right, bonny lad, I'm ready.'

Jack hears, and puts his head up the flue. Straightaway his mother chucks the cold porridge down at him. Of course, Jackie gets a face full.

'Ma,' he shouts, 'there's porridge coming down the chimney.'

'That's all right, son,' yells back his mother. 'It's raining porridge and milk out here.'

'It's tasty enough anyway,' says Jack, smacking his lips.

After that, a couple of days went by. Then the police started going round from house to house making enquiries about the landlord, asking everybody when they last saw him, what time, and such like.

Of course, they came to Jack and his mother. And they asked them questions over and over again till poor Jack didn't know whether he was coming or going, whether to stick or twist.

In the end, Jackie gave up.

'Oh, God,' he says, 'I'll tell you. I killed the landlord.'

'Oh, you killed the landlord!' says the policeman. 'And where did you put him?'

'Me and me mother buried him out the back,' says Jack. 'Come on and I'll show you.'

He takes the policeman into the back garden to the place where the grave was. His old mother traipses along behind grinning all over her face, because this was just what she knew would happen.

'Oh dear,' she says quietly to the police, 'just listen to that poor lad. He doesn't know what he's talking about. It's not right,' she says. 'You shouldn't be asking him. He'll say owt to anything.'

She shakes her old head and clicks her tongue and looks sorrowful.

'But,' she says with a sigh, 'you'd best dig up the grave. Though, mind you, you'll get a surprise.'

'Now, mother,' says Jack, 'you hold your tongue. I killed

the landlord and me and you buried him here.'

'Well, well, bonny lad,' says the old woman, 'it's all right. Don't fret yourself. You just tell me this. What day was it you killed the landlord?'

'God help us,' says Jack, 'I remember all too well. It was the day when it rained porridge and milk.'

'Rained porridge and milk?' says the police.

'Aye, that's right,' says Jack. 'You remember that?'

'My God,' says the policeman. 'The poor lad's not all there. Still, I'll have to dig up this bit he says is the grave. Just to make sure, like, you see.'

'You please yourself,' says Jack's mother.

So the policeman set to and dug up the ground where Jack had pointed. And it wasn't long before he reached the billy-goat and started to pull it out by the horns.

Jackie, the poor fool, watched with his eyes popping.

'Well I'll go to blazes,' he says. 'Landlord's grown horns and whiskers since we buried him!'

The policeman looked at Jack and shook his head.

'Poor chap,' he said. 'Take no notice of him.'

And that was the end of it. The police went off to look somewhere else for the landlord. And Jack was left to keep his old mother company for the rest of her life, which is what she had wanted all the time.

NOTES AND ACKNOWLEDGEMENTS

In County Durham, where I grew up, we have a saying: 'There's nowt so funny as folk'. I remember hearing my father end his numerous stories with it, and I suppose his gusty pleasure in recounting the comic behaviour of ordinary people has infected me. At any rate, I have always enjoyed what folklore experts call jocular tales.

This collection of some of my favourites includes familiar stories that have been told for hundreds of years as well as anecdotes from our own times. Folk tales are not museum pieces preserved from days gone by. They tell about people living now as much as about people long dead, and they often begin as street-corner jokes that grow as teller after teller adds his own colour and detail. That's why I've put in some squibs and even items from newspapers. They are folk tales at their beginnings.

Where I have wanted to—for the pleasure of it or for clarification —I have retold the stories or modified them slightly. The notes below indicate what has been done: *retold* means that I have worked freely on the original source, rewriting it more or less completely; *adapted* means I have changed the source in minor ways, usually to do with the telling rather than with details of plot. Where the story is an exact reprint, I have simply stated the source.

'Three Noodles': Adapted freely from 'Two English Folk-tales' by Prof. George Stephens in *Folk-lore Record III* Pt 2. There are many variations of this story, one of the most popular of comic folk tales.

'News': Retold. Based on version in *More English Fairy Tales*: Joseph Jacobs. London, 1894. A story with many variants. (Jacobs's several fairy-tale collections are available in facsimile from Dover/Constable.)

'Pig Tale, One': Retold. Based on a postcard by Donald McGill.

'Pig Tale, Two': Retold. Based on version in *Supplementary Collection* MS: F. J. Norton, quoted in *A Dictionary of British Folk-Tales*: Katherine M. Briggs. London, 1970.

'The Dauntless Lass': Retold. Based on version recorded in *The Recreations of a Norfolk Antiquary*: W. Rye. London, 1920.

'A Day at the Seaside': Adapted slightly from the version in *Tales from "The Dalesman" 1939–1965*. Clapham, Yorks, 1966.

'What the Devil': Retold from version in *National Tales and Legends*: W. Carew Hazlitt. London, 1899.

'Work Horse': Adapted from version in 'Some Humorous English Folk Tales' Part Two, *Folk-lore*, LIV.

'The Contrairy Wife': Adapted from 'Some Humorous English Folk Tales' Part One, *Folk-lore*, XLIX.

'The Twins': Adapted freely from 'Some Humorous English Folk Tales', Part One, op. cit.

'Miles Per Cow': Retold. Gloucestershire version told me by Jay Williams, September 1975.

'The Gaffers of Gotham': Retold from versions in *Shakespeare Jest-Books*.

'The Tramp and the Rich Man': Retold. A story found in many variations of setting, characters and details.

'Nuts': Retold from *Shakespeare Jest-Books*, op. cit.

'Start and Finish': From *Tales from the Fens*: W. H. Barrett. London, 1963.

'Coxhall Jobs': Compilation based on Katherine Briggs, op. cit., with addition of concluding retort ascribed to Ebington, Glos., in *The Folklore of the Cotswolds*: Katherine Briggs. London, 1974.

'The Merry Monk': Version told by his father to the author in *Folk Tales of Yorkshire*, H. L. Gee. London, 1952.

'Last Word'; Retold from oral source, name unknown.

'The Drunken Clerk': Retold from version in *All Round the Wrekin*: Walter White. London, 1860.

'Three Old Men of Painswick': From *Notes and Queries*, 1872.

'Irish Stakes': Retold. A typical 'Irish' joke based in this version on a memorable telling by Dave Allen, the comedian.

'Has Plummocks Legs?': Adapted from *Cornhill Magazine*, IX, 1864.

'Two Clever by Half': Retold from *Amusing Prose Chap-books*: R. H. Cunningham. London, 1889.

'Table Manners': A familiar joke.

'Sir Gammer Vans': From *Popular Rhymes and Nursery Tales*: James Orchard Halliwell. London, 1849.

'Know Me . . .': From *Tales from 'The Dalesman'*, op. cit.

'Just Good Lads': Adapted from report first published in the *Daily Express*.

'Mr Pengelly, the Devil and a Tramp': Adapted from two incidents recounted in *The Vicar of Morwenstow*: Sabine Baring Gould. London, 1876.

'Marking the Spot': Adapted freely from version quoted by Katherine Briggs, op. cit., from Norton Collection, IV.

'The Barber's Clever Wife': From *Wide-Awake Stories*: Flora Annie Steel. London, 1884. (Reissued under the title *Tales of the Punjab* by the Bodley Head, London, 1973 and reproduced by permission.)

'The Cautious Farm Boy': Retold from version in *The Villages of the White Horse*: Alfred Williams. London, 1913.

'The Irishman's Hat': Adapted from a version in *Folk-lore*, XLIX.

'Letters to the Editor': 'Trouble with Cockroaches' from the *New Scientist*; 'Potatogram' from *The Times*.

'Lazy Jack': From *Popular Rhymes and Nursery Tales*, op. cit.

'A Good Trencher': From the *Daily Express*.

'Farmer Gag's Clever Son': Adapted from 'Folk-lore of the Wye Valley' by Margaret Eyre in *Folk-lore*, XVI.

'Horse's Egg': Adapted. A story with many variations, this one based on the version in *Sussex Folk and Sussex Ways*: J. Coker Egerton. London, 1892.

'The Iron Man': Adapted from reports in *News Review* and a Mississippi paper quoted in *Funny Ha Ha and Funny Peculiar*: ed. Denys Parsons. London, 1965.

'Work Like a Good 'Un': from 'Four Yorkshire Tales' by S. O. Addy in *Folk-lore* VIII.

'Parson Spry's Bicycle': Retold from version in *Hearthside Stories of West Cornwall*: William Bottrell. Penzance, 1870.

'Get Your Hair Cut': Retold from a version I heard as a child.

'Decoy Ducks': Retold from *Tales from 'The Dalesman'*, op. cit.

'Mechanical Fault': from the *Evening Standard*.

'A Pottle O' Brains': Adapted slightly from *Folk-lore* II as quoted in *More English Fairy Tales*, op. cit.

'The Mean Farmer's Apples': Retold from a version recorded in the *Evening Standard*.

'Master of All Masters': Retold from version in *English Fairy Tales*: Joseph Jacobs. London, 1889. There are many variants.

'The Devil and the Tailor': From *The Black Knight of Ashton*: W. E. A. Axon, Manchester, 1870.

'No Clock': Adapted from *Lancashire Life and Character*: Frank Ormerod. Rochdale, 1915.

'Hereafterthis': From *More English Fairy Tales*, op. cit.

'Messingham Bells': Retold. Recorded in *Ecclesiastical Curiosities*: ed. W. Andrews. London, 1899.

'You Do My Job, I'll Do Yours': From *Popular Tales from the Norse*:

P. C. Asbjornsen and J. E. Moe. Edinburgh, 1859. (Reissued by the Bodley Head, 1969).

'Who's Crazy Now?': Retold from *The Villages of the White Horse*, op. cit.

'Buyer and Seller': Retold. Numerous versions and variations are still commonly recounted.

'Carriage Paid': Adapted from *The Everyday Book*: William Hone, quoted in *Funny Ha Ha and Funny Peculiar*, op. cit.

'Notice to All Employees': From the *Daily Express* report of a notice used by Spielman Chevrolet Company of New York.

'Hudden and Dudden and Donald O'Neary' From *Celtic Fairy Tales*: Joseph Jacobs, London, 1892.

'Silly Jack and the Landlord': Retold from version recorded by the School of Scottish Studies and quoted in *A Dictionary of British Folk-Tales*, op. cit. I have envisaged the setting as Tyneside.

I would like to record my particular debt to Katherine Briggs, whose expert work in such publications as her *Dictionary of British Folk-Tales* (Routledge and Kegan Paul, 1970/71) has increased the pleasure and eased the difficulties of such amateur folklorists as myself.

The Phantom Tollbooth

NORTON JUSTER

'It seems to me that almost everything is a waste of time,' Milo remarks as he walks dejectedly home from school. But his glumness soon turns to surprise when he unwraps a mysterious package marked ONE GENUINE PHANTOM TOLLBOOTH. Once through the Phantom Tollboth Milo has no more time to be bored for before him lies the strange land of the Kingdom of Wisdom and a series of even stranger adventures when he meets the watchdog Tock who ticks, King Azaz the unabridged the unhappy ruler of Dictionopolis, Faintly Macabre the not so wicked Which, the Whether Man and the threadbare Excuse, among a collection of the most logically illogical characters ever met on this side or that side of reality.

For readers of ten upwards.

The Haunted Mountain

MOLLIE HUNTER

Long ago in the wild Highlands of Scotland lived McAllister, a big handsome man as strong as a pine tree. But so stubborn was he to run his own life that he defied the sidhe, the evil fairy folk. Now this was a reckless thing to do, for the sidhe seeking revenge, imprisoned him inside the massive mountain of Ben MacDui. The sidhe, however, had not reckoned on the determination of Fergus his son, who gradually grew to realise that unless he rescued his father, the Great Grey Man of the haunted mountain would keep him forever.

Mollie Hunter won a Scottish Arts Council Award in 1973 for this powerful fantasy for nine-year-olds and upwards.

Dominic

WILLIAM STEIG

'What a wonderful world,' thought Dominic as he set out, all senses alert, on the highroad to adventure. And when he met the witch-alligator he quickly took her advice. 'Up this road,' she said, 'things will happen that you could never have guessed at – marvellous, unbelievable things. Up this way is where adventure is.' Now up that road and round the corner lurked the notorious Doomsday Gang, ready and scheming to trick passersby. But in Dominic, a talented dog inspired by action, they finally met their match.

William Steig, winner of the Caldecott Award, has written and illustrated this fantasy for children of nine and up.

The Tree that Sat Down

BEVERLEY NICHOLS

Once upon a time, deep in an enchanted forest, Judy helped her old grandmother run The Shop under the Willow Tree, which sold everything from used birds' nests and new quills for porcupines to medicine for sick animals. But the peaceful life in the wood is suddenly disrupted when Sam and charming Miss Smith, who is really a witch in disguise, open a rival shop which lures the customers away. When Judy discovers that Sam is not only cheating the animals, but also plotting her own destruction, she resolves to save the wood from their wickedness.

Beverley Nichols' woodland fantasy trilogy will enchant readers of nine and up.

The Stream That Stood Still and *The Mountain of Magic* are also available in Lions.

Harriet the Spy

LOUISE FITZHUGH

Harriet the Spy has a secret notebook which she fills with utterly honest jottings about her parents, her friends and her neighbours. This, she feels sure, will prepare her for her career as a famous writer. Every day on her spy route, she scrutinizes, observes and notes down anything of interest to her:

Laura Peters is thinner and uglier. I think she could do with some braces on her teeth.

Once I thought I wanted to be Franca. But she's so dull if I was her I couldn't stand myself, I guess it's not money that makes people dull. I better find out because I might be it.

If Marion Hawthorne doesn't watch out she's going to grow up into a lady Hitler.

But Harriet commits the unforgivable for a spy – she is unmasked. When her notebook is found by her school friends, their anger and retaliation and Harriet's unexpected responses explode in an hilarious and often touching way.

'Harriet M. Welsch is one of the meatiest heroines in modern juvenile literature. This novel is a *tour de force*.'

Library Journal

'This devastatingly shrewd, ruefully comic picture of the young makes a good many characters in children's fiction seem like wet dish-cloths.'

Sunday Times

The Third Class Genie

ROBERT LEESON

Disasters were leading two nil on Alec's disaster-triumph scorecard, when he slipped into the vacant factory lot, locally known as the Tank. Ginger Wallace was hot on his heels, ready to destroy him, and Alec had escaped just in the nick of time. There were disasters awaiting him at home too, when he discovered that he would have to move out of his room and into the boxroom. And, of course, there was school . . .

But Alec's luck changed when he found a beer can that was still sealed, but obviously empty. Stranger still, when he held it up to his ear, he could hear a faint snoring . . . When Alec finally opened the mysterious can, something happened that gave triumphs a roaring and most unexpected lead.

A hilarious story for readers of ten upwards.